A Christmas Anthology

Money donated to Traidcraft Exchange from the sale of this book could help small-scale farmers and producers in the developing world gain the confidence, knowledge and skills needed to trade their way out of poverty. See p. 134 for Traidcraft stories of Christmas around the world.

To find out more about how you can help Traidcraft create a world free from the scandal of poverty where all people and their communities can flourish, visit: www.traidcraft.org.uk

Traidcraft Exchange - registered charity number 1048752

TRAIDCRAFT
Fighting poverty through trade

A Christmas Anthology

Edited by Simon Danes

TRAIDCRAFT
Fighting poverty through trade

ST MARK'S PRESS

Published by St Mark's Press, 20 Close Road, Pavenham, MK43 7PP, UK

Printed and bound in the UK by The Good News Press

www.stmarkspress.com

CONTENTS

Short Stories

Poetry

Miscellany

.

Short stories

Whatever Became of Tiny Tim?

John Mortimer

'I never keep Christmas. In fact, I throw it away. I always found that if you kept Christmas it went bad quite quickly.' The speaker was Sir Timothy Cratchit, entertaining his guests at lunch in the shade of a spreading fig tree in the courtyard of his new home in a North African town. Outside, the high midday sun beat remorselessly against the white walls, sending the most prosperous beggars, those with financially opportune deformities, to shelter in the shade of painted doorways. From the minaret of a mosque, where storks had built their high-piled nests, the call to prayer was carried away on a dry wind from the Sahara. It was Christmas Day in the year 1894...

'That is why,' Sir Timothy continued, 'I have chosen to live in a country without holly, or snow, or carol singers.'

He was a short, grey-haired man whose phenomenal success in the City had led to a knighthood and early retirement. A childhood illness had left him lame, but thanks to a brilliant Harley Street surgeon, he could walk with no more help than that of the silver-topped ebony cane that now lay on the flagstones beside his chair. 'Above all, in a country without turkey.' He selected a peach from a bowl held by a pool-eyed young Arab in a white djellaba and began to peel it carefully.

'When I was a child some foolish fellow gave us a huge beast of a turkey, a bird about the size of a brontosaurus, for Christmas. Cold turkey, turkey pies, turkey rissoles; it seemed we lived on nothing else until the springtime.'

'I also ignore Christmas.' One of the guests was pale and overweight, with dark, curling hair parted in the middle. He spoke in a curious Irish singsong, with many high notes and dramatic pauses. 'And as there is no Christmas Day here, one feels no need to go about doing good deeds for the poor. No turkey and no good deeds. What a happy escape we have made from London.'

There was a ripple of laughter around the table; only Wilde's fair-haired friend, the one he referred to as Bosie, looked his usual sullen self. Sir Timothy was smiling as he watched, with some amusement, the efforts of an even smaller Arab servant, perhaps no more than 10 years old, to lift a jeroboam of Dom Perignon and fill the tall flute glasses.

'Oscar's always doing good deeds for the poor.' Bosie's voice was high and complaining. 'On the way here he gave away his watch and his cigarette case to horrible street urchins!'

'Only the undeserving poor, God bless them.' Wilde held up a large white hand in a kind of benediction. 'I give to the little pickpockets to save them the hard labour of stealing.'

'And what about the deserving poor?' a French novelist with a lean face and guilt-filled eyes, doing his best to avoid the provocative glances of the elder waiter, asked. 'What about them?'

'In my opinion,' the elderly Colonel Picton (military aide to the Bey) growled, 'they thoroughly deserve all they get.'

'Poverty will be abolished under socialism.' Wilde dwelt on the syllables with delight. 'And a good thing too. We shall all be saved the terrible bore of having to feel sorry for people.'

'I can manage that without the doubtful blessing of socialism.' Sir Timothy leaned back in his chair and felt the sunlight, creeping through the fig leaves, caress his face. 'Now let's change the subject, shall we? In this wonderfully pagan retreat, on this Christmas Day, what need have we to waste one happy moment thinking about the poor?'

And then, in spite of the sun's warmth and the comforting champagne, he shivered, as though at some chilling memory he couldn't entirely escape.

It was as though he felt again the numbing cold of a London street and the weight of an iron on his small, crippled leg. He watched his father, his long white muffler flying behind him in the wind, sliding on a patch of ice in Cornhill, and he remembered wondering, with a calm intelligence far beyond his years, how a grown man could behave so childishly. He remembered feeling ill, very ill, and seeing the tear-stained faces of his family and thinking how oppressive their looks of pity were. He made some pious remark about the Christian miracles, in order to cheer them up and encourage them to leave him alone.

Then he remembered the monstrous bird that had arrived from Ebenezer Scrooge, his father's employer, and the tears, this time of joy, his lachrymose family had shed over the vast cadaver. He remembered his father's rise in salary, pitifully small he now realized, which had finally released his leg from its fetters.

He remembered when he got his first job in Scrooge's office and became the most junior member of Scrooge & Marley. It soon became obvious to him that Ebenezer Scrooge, once a ruthless and successful businessman, had gone soft since the fatal Christmas when he was suddenly converted to good works. He no longer foreclosed mortgages or bankrupted his debtors. The bad debts multiplied and a substantial part of the profits of his business was wiped out by charitable donations, including a large sum spent on 'P.O.C.T.N.' (the Provision of Christmas Turkeys to the Needy).

At the age of 17 Timothy Cratchit made it his business to hang about the exchange, performing small errands for

Ebenezer. And because he was young and appeared harmless, he overheard much gossip and many valuable rumours. One day he borrowed the Turkey Fund (over which he had been given control), invested it for a month in Oriental Railways and made a 200 per cent profit before the company crashed. From then on nobody called him Tiny Tim. He had taken his first step toward that private fortune that would enable him to buy out Ebenezer, retire his father on an adequate but by no means generous pension and be rewarded with a title for services to the Conservative Party. He had never married, having had, he thought, quite enough of family life in his early and unhappy years.

He was a child of the hungry 1840's and a rich man in the frivolous 90's. He had known grinding poverty and gargantuan overeating. Released from both, he had turned to Art. He read The Yellow Book and collected Beardsley drawings, William Morris furniture and the plaintive townscapes of James McNeill Whistler. He visited Paris and Vienna and the Cafe Royal, where he sat at a marble-topped table, smoked flat Egyptian cigarettes and heard Wilde tell a story that appealed to him greatly. It was about a charismatic young actor who, appearing on the stage, announced that there was a small fire in the theatre but that the audience should keep calm and remain seated. Reassured by his heroic composure, the audience sat still, allowing the actor to walk out to safety. Then they were all burned to death.

Delighted by this anecdote, Sir Timothy sought, and won, the great dramatist's friendship. It was Wilde who had told him of the delights of North Africa. So he had restored an old vizier's palace near to the sea, a place full of fountains and mosaics and cool rooms and silent, smiling servants. It was a home such as neither Bob Cratchit nor Ebenezer Scrooge had ever dreamed of.

It was when he had reached this point in the quick

pursuit of memory that Sir Timothy was startled by a crash and the sound of broken glass. The younger waiter had dropped the huge bottle of Dom Perignon on the flagstones, and his small feet were surrounded by green shards and a sea of fizz.

It was a question of buying a goodbye present for Wilde, who was going back to London for the rehearsals of *The Importance of Being Earnest*. 'Don't give me anything in good taste, dear boy,' his guest had said in a prophetic moment. 'Too much good taste leads to prison.' So Sir Timothy was in one of the better shops in the casbah, bargaining for a dagger with a jewel-encrusted handle, an object of genuine vulgarity, which Wilde could use as a paper knife. As he left the shop his sleeve was plucked by an Arab boy, about the age he had been when he did his first business deal, who, speaking French, begged him to follow him to a place where even brighter, far cheaper jewels were on offer.

There was something strangely appealing about this youth, a particular charm that Sir Timothy hadn't discovered in many previous encounters, and, having given instructions that the dagger should be sent to his house and carefully guarded, he followed the young man through the maze of passageways that smelled of musk and spices, avoiding goats and beggars and importuning shopkeepers, to a tiny mud-walled dwelling on a scrubby patch of land outside the town walls.

As he stooped (and he was short) to get in the doorway, he saw, in the shadows, not the pile of rugs and inviting cushions he had expected, but an extended family, so large that it seemed likely to burst the fragile walls. Old women and girls, old men, young men and boys were sitting in grim silence, broken only by the moans of those women who were weeping with some restraint. There seemed to be no furniture, only one scrawny chicken that clucked about the floor and a dog that stretched itself, showing every rib as it did so.

It was the last scene he wished to see on Christmas Day, and he was about to turn away when he saw a child barring his way out. It was the tiny waiter, the little Arab who had dropped the champagne, not much older, Sir Timothy thought uncomfortably, than he had been on the night of the momentous turkey. Even then he would have pushed his way out, but the boy who had led him there started to explain rapidly.

Little Mahmoud had lost his post with Milord Anglais because he had dropped a bottle of wine. He was, it appeared, the sole wage earner of his enormous family. If the Milord would give him back his position Mahmoud would never, never again, drop anything, however heavy. He would, moreover, work twice as hard and for half the wages. Sir Timothy paused for a moment, looking at the child in whom he saw something of his former self; but then the family spokesman ended his plea unwisely. 'Soyez gentil, Milord. Souvenez-vous, c'est Noel.' At which Sir Timothy raised his ebony cane to clear himself a passage and limped as fast as he could out of the hovel.

That night, the night of the 25th of December, the wind changed and blew from the mountains. There was a clap of thunder and flashes of lightning across the sea and the city. The dagger had been presented and Wilde and Bosie had gone down to the harbour after dinner, quarrelling. Sir Timothy went to bed, sleepy from pigeons in almond paste and pink wine from Meknes. He had been bored by his servants' exhibition of belly dancing and had fallen asleep quickly. Within an hour, it seemed to him, he was awake again.

At first he thought it was only his bed curtains stirring in the wind, and then, as lightning cracked across the windowpanes, he saw two figures looking down at him. The first was tall and stately, shrouded in a black garment that concealed its head, its face, its form, and left nothing

14

visible but one outstretched hand. The other was an elderly, hatchet-faced man with grey whiskers, who wore a nightgown and bedroom slippers and had on a white woolen cap to cover his baldness. Sir Timothy had no difficulty in recognizing Ebenezer Scrooge, who had died over 30 years before in his retirement home in Brighton. 'The time has come, Timothy,' Scrooge said in the high, snuffling voice that had been his when he was alive, 'for you to meet the Ghost of Christmas Yet to Come.'

'Oscar, Bosie!' Sir Timothy sat up in bed, rubbing his eyes. 'How tremendously amusing. And what excellent get-ups. Bosie's even got Scrooge's voice, but God knows how.'

'Don't pretend you don't know us.' The figure of Scrooge passed through the solid bedpost as though it were a flicker of light. 'And whom are you calling to? I heard you were cultivating exotic company.'

'Is that truly you, Scrooge?' Sir Timothy had never, in his most risky business dealings, shown fear, and faced with these figures of death he was more curious than overawed. 'And are you truly dead?'

'As truly as you will be, Tiny Tim.'

'So, even beyond the grave, must you be forever prattling about Christmas?'

'We are to be given a vision,' Scrooge told him, 'of a Christmas to Come. I haven't yet seen it and so we are both privileged.'

'What on earth have you been doing all these years, Scrooge, if you haven't seen this vision you promise me? Forcing turkey down the throats of reluctant seraphim?'

But before Scrooge could reply to his blasphemous suggestion, the room was illuminated by lightning again and the silent Spirit pointed a long and bony finger at the window. Sir Timothy felt Scrooge's cold hand fasten round his wrist like a fetter and, with supernatural strength, Scrooge pulled him out of bed and toward the window.

'Where do you want me to go?' he managed, in his astonishment at this violent arrest, to ask.

'Over a century away.' The Spirit spoke in low, resonant tones. 'Come!' And then, as the casement rattled and flew open in the wind, the three of them seemed to float out of it as though they had lost all earthly weight.

The sights he saw on the journey would remain with Sir Timothy for the rest of his life, and even haunt his spirit after death, as they had troubled the ghost of Ebenezer Scrooge.

At first they flew across Africa, in the early light of dawn, over earth that would no longer bear crops, where little children in the thousands, with great, bald heads, swollen bodies and matchstick limbs, died in the arms of their starving mothers. In the same land they saw capitalist and socialist politicians, equally corrupt and uncaring, who had enriched themselves and their well-fed soldiers. They saw scenes of massacre and torture that seemed to have no reason but the wilful longing to extinguish life.

They flew over the Arab countries and into Europe and saw guns everywhere, sold to every villager determined to kill his neighbour. In countries that had once been civilized they saw women ravished and children bombed and strangled. They saw the poor supplies of food provided by charity stolen by robbers or politicians and sold to the highest bidder. Flitting across more prosperous countries, they saw mountains of butter, great stores of wheat and wine, and heard a congress of finance ministers explain that they couldn't possibly afford to send food to the starving multitudes. With the speed of a sigh they crossed a great ocean and came to a country where the young killed and robbed for drugs and windows were smashed and shops left burning. In one such looted store they saw the tinsel hanging, the torn streamers, the few gifts that had not been stolen, the tawdry remains of Christmas Day.

And then they were back, after no time had passed or else a hundred years, in Sir Timothy's bedroom. As they stood at the foot of his bed, the ghost of Scrooge and the ghost of future Christmases, the man who had, long ago, been Tiny Tim looked at them, greatly troubled.

'You showed me what I had no desire to see,' he protested.

'When the time comes everyone will see all of that, and more,' the Spirit boomed. 'They will have devices for looking at it that they will not be able to resist using. Everyone's living room will be filled with the suffering of the world.'

'When shall I die?' Sir Timothy dared to ask.

'Christmas Day, 1922. In time for the Great War but too early for television. You will suffer a heart attack after dinner in Raffles Hotel, Singapore.'

'Then I shall be spared the sight of all that misery?'

'Not necessarily. Ebenezer Scrooge died many years ago and tonight I showed it all to him. He has to learn that the provision of turkeys is no answer. There simply aren't enough turkeys to go round.'

'I could have told him that.' Sir Timothy was encouraged to find himself in agreement with the Spirit. 'Giving turkeys doesn't really do much good.'

'But what does? What does good, in your opinion?' The Spirit had moved very close to him, so close that he could see a pair of deep-set, smouldering eyes in the shadows under its hood.

'I'm not sure.' Sir Timothy faltered, now afraid. 'I'll give Mahmoud back his job. Will that be something?'

'Something, I suppose. But not very much. All I can tell you to do is to look about you. See everything, however much it distresses you or even turns your stomach. So men and women like you may change a little. It's all we can hope for. We shall leave you now.' The Spirit and the ghost of the old man began to move toward

17

the window. Sir Timothy sat on his bed and watched them with considerable relief, but the last words of the Spirit made him shiver. 'We shall go out again in a year's time and see if there's been any improvement.'

The open window banged again in the wind and his extraordinary visitors were gone. Still in the Sulka nightshirt in which he'd gone round the world, Sir Timothy crept back into bed and pulled the embroidered covers over him. It was only, he thought with genuine terror, 364 days till next Christmas.

The Signal-Man

Charles Dickens

The Signal-Man was originally published in the 1866 Christmas edition of the periodical edited by Dickens, All The Year Round.

'Halloa! Below there!'

When he heard a voice thus calling to him, he was standing at the door of his box, with a flag in his hand, furled round its short pole. One would have thought, considering the nature of the ground, that he could not have doubted from what quarter the voice came; but instead of looking up to where I stood on the top of the steep cutting nearly over his head, he turned himself about, and looked down the Line. There was something remarkable in his manner of doing so, though I could not have said for my life what. But I know it was remarkable enough to attract my notice, even though his figure was foreshortened and shadowed, down in the deep trench, and mine was high above him, so steeped in the glow of an angry sunset, that I had shaded my eyes with my hand before I saw him at all.

'Halloa! Below!'

From looking down the Line, he turned himself about again, and, raising his eyes, saw my figure high above him.

'Is there any path by which I can come down and speak to you?'

He looked up at me without replying, and I looked down at him without pressing him too soon with a repetition of my idle question. Just then there came a vague vibration in the earth and air, quickly changing into a violent pulsation, and an oncoming rush that caused me to start back, as though it had force to draw me down. When such vapour as rose to my height from this rapid train had passed me, and was skimming away over the landscape, I looked down again, and saw him refurling the flag he had shown while the train went by.

I repeated my inquiry. After a pause, during which he seemed to regard me with fixed attention, he motioned with his rolled-up flag towards a point on my level, some two or three hundred yards distant. I called down to him, 'All right!' and made for that point. There, by dint of looking closely about me, I found a rough zigzag descending path notched out, which I followed.

The cutting was extremely deep, and unusually precipitate. It was made through a clammy stone, that became oozier and wetter as I went down. For these reasons, I found the way long enough to give me time to recall a singular air of reluctance or compulsion with which he had pointed out the path.

When I came down low enough upon the zigzag descent to see him again, I saw that he was standing between the rails on the way by which the train had lately passed, in an attitude as if he were waiting for me to appear. He had his left hand at his chin, and that left elbow rested on his right hand, crossed over his breast. His attitude was one of such expectation and watchfulness that I stopped a moment, wondering at it.

I resumed my downward way, and stepping out upon the level of the railroad, and drawing nearer to him, saw that he was a dark sallow man, with a dark beard and rather heavy eyebrows. His post was in as solitary and dismal a place as ever I saw. On either side, a dripping-wet wall of jagged stone, excluding all view but a strip of sky; the perspective one way only a crooked prolongation of this great dungeon; the shorter perspective in the other direction terminating in a gloomy red light, and the gloomier entrance to a black tunnel, in whose massive architecture there was a barbarous, depressing, and forbidding air. So little sunlight ever found its way to this spot, that it had an earthy, deadly smell; and so much cold wind rushed through it, that it struck chill to me, as if I had left the natural world.

Before he stirred, I was near enough to him to have touched him. Not even then removing his eyes from mine, he stepped back one step, and lifted his hand.

This was a lonesome post to occupy (I said), and it had riveted my attention when I looked down from up yonder. A visitor was a rarity, I should suppose; not an unwelcome rarity, I hoped? In me, he merely saw a man who had been shut up within narrow limits all his life, and who, being at last set free, had a newly-awakened interest in these great works. To such purpose I spoke to him; but I am far from sure of the terms I used; for, besides that I am not happy in opening any conversation, there was something in the man that daunted me.

He directed a most curious look towards the red light near the tunnel's mouth, and looked all about it, as if something were missing from it, and then looked it me.

That light was part of his charge? Was it not?

He answered in a low voice, – 'Don't you know it is?'

The monstrous thought came into my mind, as I perused the fixed eyes and the saturnine face, that this was a spirit, not a man. I have speculated since, whether there may have been infection in his mind.

In my turn, I stepped back. But in making the action, I detected in his eyes some latent fear of me. This put the monstrous thought to flight.

'You look at me,' I said, forcing a smile, 'as if you had a dread of me.'

'I was doubtful,' he returned, 'whether I had seen you before.'

'Where?'

He pointed to the red light he had looked at.

'There?' I said.

Intently watchful of me, he replied (but without sound), 'Yes.'

'My good fellow, what should I do there? However, be that as it may, I never was there, you may swear.'

'I think I may,' he rejoined. 'Yes; I am sure I may.'

His manner cleared, like my own. He replied to my remarks with readiness, and in well-chosen words. Had he much to do there? Yes; that was to say, he had enough responsibility to bear; but exactness and watchfulness were what was required of him, and of actual work – manual labour – he had next to none. To change that signal, to trim those lights, and to turn this iron handle now and then, was all he had to do under that head. Regarding those many long and lonely hours of which I seemed to make so much, he could only say that the routine of his life had shaped itself into that form, and he had grown used to it. He had taught himself a language down here, – if only to know it by sight, and to have formed his own crude ideas of its pronunciation, could be called learning it. He had also worked at fractions and decimals, and tried a little algebra; but he was, and had been as a boy, a poor hand at figures. Was it necessary for him when on duty always to remain in that channel of damp air, and could he never rise into the sunshine from between those high stone walls? Why, that depended upon times and circumstances. Under some conditions there would be less upon the Line than under others, and the same held good as to certain hours of the day and night. In bright weather, he did choose occasions for getting a little above these lower shadows; but, being at all times liable to be called by his electric bell, and at such times listening for it with redoubled anxiety, the relief was less than I would suppose.

He took me into his box, where there was a fire, a desk for an official book in which he had to make certain entries, a telegraphic instrument with its dial, face, and needles, and the little bell of which he had spoken. On my trusting that he would excuse the remark that he had been well educated, and (I hoped I might say without offence) perhaps educated above that station, he observed that instances of slight incongruity in such wise would rarely be found wanting among large bodies of men; that he had heard it was so in workhouses, in the police force, even in that last desperate resource, the army; and that he knew it was so, more or less, in any great railway staff. He had been, when young (if I could believe it, sitting in that hut, – he scarcely could), a student of natural philosophy, and had attended lectures; but he had run wild, misused his opportunities, gone down, and never risen again. He had no complaint to offer about that. He had made his bed, and he lay upon it. It was far too late to make another.

All that I have here condensed he said in a quiet manner, with his grave dark regards divided between me and the fire. He threw in the word, 'Sir,' from time to time, and especially when he referred to his youth, – as though to request me to understand that he claimed to be nothing but what I found him. He was several times interrupted by the little bell, and had to read off messages, and send replies. Once he had to stand without the door, and display a flag as a train passed, and make some verbal communication to the driver. In the discharge of his duties, I observed him to be remarkably exact and vigilant, breaking off his discourse at a syllable, and remaining silent until what he had to do was done.

In a word, I should have set this man down as one of the safest of men to be employed in that capacity, but for the circumstance that while he was speaking to me he twice broke off with a fallen colour, turned his face towards the little bell when it did NOT ring, opened the door of the hut (which was kept shut to exclude the unhealthy damp), and looked out towards the red light near the mouth of the tunnel. On both of those occasions, he came back to the fire with the inexplicable air upon him which I had remarked, without being able to define, when we were so far asunder.

Said I, when I rose to leave him, 'You almost make me think that I have met with a contented man.'

(I am afraid I must acknowledge that I said it to lead him on.)

'I believe I used to be so,' he rejoined, in the low voice in which he had first spoken; 'but I am troubled, sir, I am troubled.'

He would have recalled the words if he could. He had said them, however, and I took them up quickly.

'With what? What is your trouble?'

'It is very difficult to impart, sir. It is very, very difficult to speak of. If ever you make me another visit, I will try to tell you.'

'But I expressly intend to make you another visit. Say, when shall it be?'

'I go off early in the morning, and I shall be on again at ten to-morrow night, sir.'

'I will come at eleven.'

He thanked me, and went out at the door with me. 'I'll show my white light, sir,' he said, in his peculiar low voice, 'till you have found the way up. When you have found it, don't call out! And when you are at the top, don't call out!'

His manner seemed to make the place strike colder to me, but I said no more than, 'Very well.'

'And when you come down to-morrow night, don't call out! Let me ask you a parting question. What made you cry, "Halloa! Below there!" to-night?'

'Heaven knows,' said I. 'I cried something to that effect —'

'Not to that effect, sir. Those were the very words. I know them well.'

'Admit those were the very words. I said them, no doubt, because I saw you below.'

'For no other reason?'

'What other reason could I possibly have?'

'You had no feeling that they were conveyed to you in any supernatural way?'

'No.'

He wished me good-night, and held up his light. I walked by the side of the down Line of rails (with a very disagreeable sensation of a train coming behind me) until I found the path. It was easier to mount than to descend, and I got back to my inn without any adventure.

Punctual to my appointment, I placed my foot on the first notch of the zigzag next night, as the distant clocks were striking eleven. He was waiting for me at the bottom, with his white light on. 'I have not called out,' I said, when we came close together; 'may I speak now?' 'By all means, sir.' 'Good-night, then, and here's my hand.' 'Good-night, sir, and here's mine.' With that we walked side by side to his box, entered it, closed the door, and sat down by the fire.

'I have made up my mind, sir,' he began, bending forward as soon as we were seated, and speaking in a tone but a little above a whisper, 'that you shall not have to ask me twice what troubles me. I took you for some one else yesterday evening. That troubles me.'

'That mistake?'

'No. That some one else.'

'Who is it?'

'I don't know.'

'Like me?'

'I don't know. I never saw the face. The left arm is across the face, and the right arm is waved, – violently waved. This way.'

I followed his action with my eyes, and it was the action of an arm gesticulating, with the utmost passion and vehemence, 'For God's sake, clear the way!'

'One moonlight night,' said the man, 'I was sitting here, when I heard a voice cry, "Halloa! Below there!" I started up, looked from that door, and saw this Some one else standing by the red light near the tunnel, waving as I just now showed you. The voice seemed hoarse with shouting, and it cried, "Look out! Look out!" And then again, "Halloa! Below there! Look out!" I caught up my lamp, turned it on red, and ran towards the figure, calling, "What's wrong? What has happened? Where?" It stood just outside the blackness of the tunnel. I advanced so close upon it that I wondered at its keeping the sleeve across its eyes. I ran right up at it, and had my hand stretched out to pull the sleeve away, when it was gone.'

'Into the tunnel?' said I.

'No. I ran on into the tunnel, five hundred yards. I stopped, and held my lamp above my head, and saw the figures of the measured distance, and saw the wet stains stealing down the walls and trickling through the arch. I ran out again faster than I had run in (for I had a mortal abhorrence of the place upon me), and I looked all round the red light with my own red light, and I went up the iron ladder to the gallery atop of it, and I came down again, and ran back here. I telegraphed both ways, "An alarm has been given. Is anything wrong?" The answer came back, both ways, "All well."'

Resisting the slow touch of a frozen finger tracing out my spine, I showed him how that this figure must be a deception of his sense of sight; and how that figures, originating in disease of the delicate nerves that minister to the functions of the eye, were known to have often troubled patients, some of whom had become conscious of the nature of their affliction, and had even proved it by experiments upon themselves. 'As to an imaginary cry,' said I, 'do but listen for a moment to the wind in this unnatural valley while we speak so low, and to the wild harp it makes of the telegraph wires.'

That was all very well, he returned, after we had sat listening for a while, and he ought to know something of the wind and the wires, – he who so often passed long winter nights there, alone and watching. But he would beg to remark that he had not finished.

I asked his pardon, and he slowly added these words, touching my arm, –

'Within six hours after the Appearance, the memorable accident on this Line happened, and within ten hours the dead and wounded were brought along through the tunnel over the spot where the figure had stood.'

A disagreeable shudder crept over me, but I did my best against it. It was not to be denied, I rejoined, that this was a remarkable coincidence, calculated deeply to impress his mind. But it was unquestionable that remarkable coincidences did continually occur, and they must be taken into account in dealing with such a subject. Though to be sure I must admit, I added (for I thought I saw that he was going to bring the objection to bear upon me), men of common sense did not allow much for coincidences in making the ordinary calculations of life.

He again begged to remark that he had not finished.

I again begged his pardon for being betrayed into interruptions.

'This,' he said, again laying his hand upon my arm, and glancing over his shoulder with hollow eyes, 'was just a year ago. Six or seven months passed, and I had recovered from the surprise and shock, when one morning, as the day was breaking, I, standing at the door, looked towards the red light, and saw the spectre again.' He stopped, with a fixed look at me.

'Did it cry out?'

'No. It was silent.'

'Did it wave its arm?'

'No. It leaned against the shaft of the light, with both hands before the face. Like this.'

Once more I followed his action with my eyes. It was an action of mourning. I have seen such an attitude in stone figures on tombs.

'Did you go up to it?'

'I came in and sat down, partly to collect my thoughts, partly because it had turned me faint. When I went to the door again, daylight was above me, and the ghost was gone.'

'But nothing followed? Nothing came of this?'

He touched me on the arm with his forefinger twice or thrice giving a ghastly nod each time: –

'That very day, as a train came out of the tunnel, I noticed, at a carriage window on my side, what looked like a confusion of hands and heads, and something waved. I saw it just in time to signal the driver, Stop! He shut off, and put his brake on, but the train drifted past here a hundred and fifty yards or more. I ran after it, and, as I went along, heard terrible screams and cries. A beautiful young lady had died instantaneously in one of the compartments, and was brought in here, and laid down on this floor between us.'

Involuntarily I pushed my chair back, as I looked from the boards at which he pointed to himself.

'True, sir. True. Precisely as it happened, so I tell it you.'

I could think of nothing to say, to any purpose, and my mouth was very dry. The wind and the wires took up the story with a long lamenting wail.

He resumed. 'Now, sir, mark this, and judge how my mind is troubled. The spectre came back a week ago. Ever since, it has been there, now and again, by fits and starts.'

'At the light?'

'At the Danger-light.'

'What does it seem to do?'

He repeated, if possible with increased passion and vehemence, that former gesticulation of, 'For God's sake, clear the way!'

Then he went on. 'I have no peace or rest for it. It calls to me, for many minutes together, in an agonised manner, "Below there! Look out! Look out!" It stands waving to me. It rings my little bell – '

I caught at that. 'Did it ring your bell yesterday evening when I was here, and you went to the door?'

'Twice.'

'Why, see,' said I, 'how your imagination misleads you. My eyes were on the bell, and my ears were open to the bell, and if I am a living man, it did *not* ring at those times. No, nor at any other time, except when it was rung in the natural course of physical things by the station communicating with you.'

He shook his head. 'I have never made a mistake as to that yet, sir. I have never confused the spectre's ring with the man's. The ghost's ring is a strange vibration in the bell that it derives from nothing else, and I have not asserted that the bell stirs to the eye. I don't wonder that you failed to hear it. But I heard it.'

'And did the spectre seem to be there, when you looked out?'

'It *was* there.'

'Both times?'

He repeated firmly: 'Both times.'

'Will you come to the door with me, and look for it now?'

He bit his under lip as though he were somewhat unwilling, but arose. I opened the door, and stood on the step, while he stood in the doorway. There was the Danger-light. There was the dismal mouth of the tunnel. There were the high, wet stone walls of the cutting. There were the stars above them.

'Do you see it?' I asked him, taking particular note of his face. His eyes were prominent and strained, but not very much more so, perhaps, than my own had been when I had directed them earnestly towards the same spot.

'No,' he answered. 'It is not there.'

'Agreed,' said I.

We went in again, shut the door, and resumed our seats. I was thinking how best to improve this advantage, if it might be called one, when he took up the conversation in such a matter-of-course way, so assuming that there could be no serious question of fact between us, that I felt myself placed in the weakest of positions.

'By this time you will fully understand, sir,' he said, 'that what troubles me so dreadfully is the question, What does the spectre mean?'

I was not sure, I told him, that I did fully understand.

'What is its warning against?' he said, ruminating, with his eyes on the fire, and only by times turning them on me. 'What is the danger? Where is the danger? There is danger overhanging somewhere on the Line. Some dreadful calamity will happen. It is not to be doubted this third time, after what has gone before. But surely this is a cruel haunting of me. What can I do?'

He pulled out his handkerchief, and wiped the drops from his heated forehead.

'If I telegraph Danger, on either side of me, or on both, I can give no reason for it,' he went on, wiping the palms of his hands. 'I should get into trouble, and do no good. They would think I was mad. This is the way it would work, – Message: "Danger! Take care!" Answer: "What Danger? Where?" Message: "Don't know. But, for God's sake, take care!" They would displace me. What else could they do?'

His pain of mind was most pitiable to see. It was the mental torture of a conscientious man, oppressed beyond endurance by an unintelligible responsibility involving life.

'When it first stood under the Danger-light,' he went on, putting his dark hair back from his head, and drawing his hands outward across and across his temples in an extremity of feverish distress, 'why not tell me where that accident was to happen, – if it must happen? Why not tell me how it could be averted, – if it could have been averted? When on its second coming it hid its face, why not tell me, instead, "She is going to die. Let them keep her at home"? If it came, on those two occasions, only to show me that its warnings were true, and so to prepare me for the third, why not warn me plainly now? And I, Lord help me! A mere poor signal-man on this solitary station! Why not go to somebody with credit to be believed, and power to act?'

When I saw him in this state, I saw that for the poor man's sake, as well as for the public safety, what I had to do for the time was to compose his mind. Therefore, setting aside all question of reality or unreality between us, I represented to him that whoever thoroughly discharged his duty must do well, and that at least it was his comfort that he understood his duty, though he did not understand these confounding Appearances. In this effort I succeeded far better than in the attempt to reason him out of his conviction. He became calm; the occupations incidental to his post as the night advanced began to make larger demands on his attention: and I left him at two in the morning. I had offered to stay through the night, but he would not hear of it.

That I more than once looked back at the red light as I ascended the pathway, that I did not like the red light, and that I should have slept but poorly if my bed had been under it, I see no reason to conceal. Nor did I like the two sequences of the accident and the dead girl. I see no reason to conceal that either.

But what ran most in my thoughts was the consideration

how ought I to act, having become the recipient of this disclosure? I had proved the man to be intelligent, vigilant, painstaking, and exact; but how long might he remain so, in his state of mind? Though in a subordinate position, still he held a most important trust, and would I (for instance) like to stake my own life on the chances of his continuing to execute it with precision?

Unable to overcome a feeling that there would be something treacherous in my communicating what he had told me to his superiors in the Company, without first being plain with himself and proposing a middle course to him, I ultimately resolved to offer to accompany him (otherwise keeping his secret for the present) to the wisest medical practitioner we could hear of in those parts, and to take his opinion. A change in his time of duty would come round next night, he had apprised me, and he would be off an hour or two after sunrise, and on again soon after sunset. I had appointed to return accordingly.

Next evening was a lovely evening, and I walked out early to enjoy it. The sun was not yet quite down when I traversed the field-path near the top of the deep cutting. I would extend my walk for an hour, I said to myself, half an hour on and half an hour back, and it would then be time to go to my signal-man's box.

Before pursuing my stroll, I stepped to the brink, and mechanically looked down, from the point from which I had first seen him. I cannot describe the thrill that seized upon me, when, close at the mouth of the tunnel, I saw the appearance of a man, with his left sleeve across his eyes, passionately waving his right arm.

The nameless horror that oppressed me passed in a moment, for in a moment I saw that this appearance of a man was a man indeed, and that there was a little group of other men, standing at a short distance, to whom he seemed to be rehearsing the gesture he made. The Danger-light was not yet lighted. Against its shaft, a little low hut, entirely new to me, had been made of some wooden supports and tarpaulin. It looked no bigger than a bed.

With an irresistible sense that something was wrong, – with a flashing self-reproachful fear that fatal mischief had come of my leaving the man there, and causing no one to be sent to overlook or correct what he did, – I descended the notched path with all the speed I could make.

'What is the matter?' I asked the men.

'Signal-man killed this morning, sir.'

'Not the man belonging to that box?'

'Yes, sir.'

'Not the man I know?'

'You will recognise him, sir, if you knew him,' said the man who spoke for the others, solemnly uncovering his own head, and raising an end of the tarpaulin, 'for his face is quite composed.'

'O, how did this happen, how did this happen?' I asked, turning from one to another as the hut closed in again.

'He was cut down by an engine, sir. No man in England knew his work better. But somehow he was not clear of the outer rail. It was just at broad day. He had struck the light, and had the lamp in his hand. As the engine came out of the tunnel, his back was towards her, and she cut him down. That man drove her, and was showing how it happened. Show the gentleman, Tom.'

The man, who wore a rough dark dress, stepped back to his former place at the mouth of the tunnel.

'Coming round the curve in the tunnel, sir,' he said, 'I saw him at the end, like as if I saw him down a perspective-glass. There was no time to check speed, and I knew him to be very careful. As he didn't seem to take heed of the whistle, I shut it off when we were running down upon him, and called to him as loud as I could call.'

'What did you say?'

'I said, "Below there! Look out! Look out! For God's

sake, clear the way!"'

I started.

'Ah! it was a dreadful time, sir. I never left off calling to him. I put this arm before my eyes not to see, and I waved this arm to the last; but it was no use.'

Without prolonging the narrative to dwell on any one of its curious circumstances more than on any other, I may, in closing it, point out the coincidence that the warning of the Engine-Driver included, not only the words which the unfortunate Signal-man had repeated to me as haunting him, but also the words which I myself – not he – had attached, and that only in my own mind, to the gesticulation he had imitated.

The Widow's Mite

Anthony Trollope

Like Dickens, Trollope produced a great many Christmas stories; this one was originally published in Good Words *magazine in 1863.*

The background to the story is the Lancashire Cotton Famine of 1861 – 1865. The American Civil War had massively reduced cotton imports to the Lancashire mills, which meant huge numbers of the workforce became unemployed. A large number of relief schemes were set up to help them.

The reference for the biblical story of the widow's mite is Mark 12.41-44.

'But, I'm not a widow, and I haven't got two mites.'

'My dear, you are a widow, and you have got two mites.'

'I'll tell both of you something that will astonish you. I've made a calculation, and I find that if everybody in England would give up their Christmas dinner; that is, in Scotland and Ireland, too – '

'They never have any in Ireland, Bob.'

'Hold your tongue till I've done, Charley. They do have Christmas dinners in Ireland. It's pretty nearly the only day that they do, and I don't count much upon them either. But if everybody gave up his special Christmas dinner, and dined as he does on other days, the saving would amount to two millions and a half.'

Charley whistled.

'Two millions and a half is a large sum of money,' said Mrs Granger, the elder lady of the party.

'Those calculations never do any good,' said the younger lady, who had declared herself not to be a widow.

'Those calculations do a great deal of good,' continued Bob, carrying on his argument with continued warmth. 'They show us what a great national effort would do.'

'A little national effort I should call that,' said Mrs Granger. 'But I should doubt the two millions and a half.'

'Half a crown a head on thirty million people would do it. You are to include all the beer, wine, and whisky. But suppose you take off one-fifth for the babies and young girls, who don't drink.'

'Thank you, Bob,' said the younger lady, – Nora Field by name.

'And two more fifths for the poor, who haven't got the half-crown a head,' said the elder lady.

'And you'd ruin the grocer and butcher,' said Charley.

'And never get your half-crown after all,' said Nora.

It need hardly be said that the subject under discussion was the best mode of abstracting from the pockets of the non-suffering British public a sufficiency of money to sustain the suffering portion during the period of the cotton famine. Mr Granger was the rector of Plumstock, a parish in Cheshire, sufficiently near to the manufacturing districts to give to every incident of life at that time a colouring taken from the distress of the neighbourhood; but which had not itself ever depended on cotton, – for Plumstock boasted that it was purely agricultural. Mr Granger was the chairman of a branch relief committee, which had its centre in Liverpool, and the subject of the destitution, with the different modes by which it might be, should be, or should not be relieved, was constantly under discussion in the rectory. Mr Granger himself was a practical man, somewhat hard in his manners, but by no means hard in his heart, who had in these times taken upon himself the business of almsbegging on a large scale. He declined to look at the matter in a political, statistical, or economical point of view, and answered all questions as to rates, rates in aid, loans, and the Consolidated Fund, with a touch of sarcasm, which showed the bent of his own mind.

'I've no doubt you'll have settled all that in the wisest possible way by the time that the war is over, and the river full of cotton again.'

'Father,' Bob replied, pointing across the Cheshire flats to the Mersey, 'that river will never again be full of American cotton.'

'It will be all the same for the present purpose, if it comes from India,' said the rector, declining all present argument on the great American question. To collect alms was his immediate work, and he would do nothing else. Five-pound notes, sovereigns, half-crowns, shillings, and pence! In search of these he was urgent, we may almost say day and night, begging with a pertinacity which was disagreeable, but irresistible. The man who gave him five sovereigns, instantly became the mark for another petition. 'When you have got your dinner, you have not done with the butcher forever,' he would say in answer to reproaches. 'Of course, we must go on as long as this thing lasts.' Then his friends and neighbours buttoned up their pockets; but Mr Granger would extract coin from them even when buttoned.

The two young men who had taken part in the above argument were his sons. The elder, Charles, was at Oxford, but now in these Christmas days – for Christmas was close at hand – had come home. Bob, the second son, was in a merchant's house in Liverpool, intending to become, in the fulness of time, a British merchant prince. It had been hinted to him, however, more than once, that if he would talk a little less, and work a little harder, the path to his princedom would be quicker found than if his present habits were maintained. Nora Field was Mrs Granger's niece. She was Miss Field, and certainly not a widow in the literal sense of the word; but she was about to become a bride a few weeks after Christmas. 'It is spoil from the Amalekites,' Mr Granger had said, when she had paid in some contribution from her slender private stores to his treasury; – 'spoil from the Amalekites, and therefore the more precious.' He had called Nora Field's two sovereigns spoil from the Amalekites, because she was about to marry an American.

Frederic Frew, or Frederic F. Frew, as he delighted to hear himself called, for he had been christened Franklin as well as Frederic, – and to an American it is always a point of honour that, at any rate, the initial of his second Christian name should be remembered by all men, – was a Pennsylvanian from Philadelphia; a strong Democrat, according to the politics of his own country, hating the Republicans, as the Tories used to hate the Whigs among us, before political feeling had become extinct; speaking against Lincoln the President, and Seward his minister, and the Fremonts, and Summers, and Philipses, and Beechers of the Republican party, fine hard racy words of powerful condemnation, such as used to be spoken against Earl Grey and his followers, but nevertheless as steady for the war as Lincoln, or Seward, or any Republican of them all; – as steady for the war, and as keen in his bitterness against England. His father had been a partner in a house of business, of which the chief station had been in Liverpool. That house had now closed its transactions, and young Frew was living and intended to live an easy idle life on the moderate fortune which had been left him; but the circumstances of his family affairs had made it necessary for him to pass many months in Liverpool, and during that sojourn he had become engaged to Nora Field. He had travelled much, going everywhere with his eyes open, as Americans do. He knew many things, had read many books, and was decided in his opinion on most subjects. He was good-looking too, and well-mannered; was kindly-hearted, and capable of much generosity. But he was hard, keen in his intelligence, but not broad in his genius, thin and meagre in his aspirations, – not looking to or even desirous of anything great, but indulging a profound contempt for all that is very small. He was a well-instructed, but by no means learned man, who greatly despised those who were ignorant. I fear that he hated England in his heart; but he did not hate Nora Field, and was about to make her his wife in three or four weeks from the present time.

When Nora declared to her aunt that she was not a widow, and that she possessed no two mites, and when her aunt flatly contradicted her, stating that she was a widow, and did possess two mites, they had not intended to be understood by each other literally. It was an old dispute between them. 'What the widow gave,' said Nora, 'she gave off her own poor back, and therefore was very cold. She gave it out of her own poor mouth, and was very hungry afterwards in consequence. I have given my two pounds, but I shall not be cold or hungry. I wish I was a widow with two mites; only, the question is whether I should not keep them for my own back after all, and thus gain nothing by the move.'

'As to that,' replied her aunt, 'I cannot speak. But the widowhood and two mites are there for us all, if we choose to make use of them.'

'In these days,' said Bob, 'the widows with two mites should not be troubled at all. We can do it all without them if we go to work properly.'

'If you had read your Bible properly, sir,' said Mrs Granger, 'you would understand that the widows would not thank you for the exemption.'

'I don't want the widows to thank me. I only want to live, and allow others to live, according to the existing circumstances of the world.' It was manifest from Bob's tone that he regarded his mother as little better than an old fogy.

In January, Nora was to become Mrs Frederic F. Frew, and be at once taken away to new worlds, new politics, and new loves and hatreds. Like a true, honest-hearted girl as she was, she had already become half an American in spirit. She was an old Union American, and as such was strong against the South; and in return for her fervour in that matter, her future husband consented to abstain from any present loud abuse of things English, and generously allowed her to defend her own country when it was abused. This was much as coming from an American. Let us hope that the same privilege may be accorded to her in her future home in Philadelphia. But in the meantime, during these last weeks of her girlhood, these cold, cruel weeks of desperate want, she strove vigorously to do what little might be in her power for the poor of the country she was leaving. All this want had been occasioned by the wretched rebels of the South. This was her theory. And she was right in much of this. Whether the Americans of the South are wretched or are rebels we will not say here; but of this there can be no doubt, that they have created all this misery which we are enduring. 'But I have no way of making myself a widow,' she said again. 'Uncle Robert would not let me give away the cloak he gave me the other day.'

'He would have to give you another,' said Mrs. Granger.

'Exactly. It is not so easy, after all, to be a widow with two mites!'

Nora Field had no fortune of her own, nor was her uncle in a position to give her any. He was not a poor man; but, like many men who are not poor, he had hardly a pound of his own in the shape of ready money. To Nora and to her cousins, and to certain other first cousins of the same family, had been left, some eighteen months since, by a grand-aunt, a hundred pounds apiece, and with this hundred pounds Nora was providing for herself her wedding trousseau. A hundred pounds do not go far in such provision, as some young married women who may read this will perhaps acknowledge; but Mr Frederic F. Frew had been told all about it, and he was contented. Miss Field was fond of nice clothes, and had been tempted more than once to wish that her great-aunt had left them all two hundred pounds apiece instead of one.

'If I were to cast in my wedding veil?' said Nora.

'That will be your husband's property,' said her aunt.

'Ah, but before I'm married.'

'Then why have it at all?'

'It is ordered, you know.'

'Couldn't you bedizen yourself with one made of false lace?' said her uncle. 'Frew would never find it out, and that would be a most satisfactory spoiling of the Amalekite.'

'He isn't an Amalekite, uncle Robert. Or if he is, I'm another.'

'Just so; and therefore false lace will be quite good enough for you. Molly' – Mrs Granger's name was Molly – 'I've promised to let them have the use of the great boiler in the back-kitchen once a week, and you are to furnish them with fuel.'

'Oh, dear!' said Mrs Granger, upon whose active charity this loan of her own kitchen boiler made a strain that was almost too severe. But she recovered herself in half a minute. 'Very well, my dear. But you won't expect any dinner on that day.'

'No; I shall expect no dinner; only some food in the rough. You may boil that in the copper too, if you like it.'

'You know, my dear, you don't like anything boiled.'

'As for that, Molly, I don't suppose any of them like it. They'd all prefer roast-mutton.'

'The copper will be your two mites,' whispered the niece.

'Only I have not thrown them in of my accord,' said

Mrs Granger.

Mr Frew, who was living in Liverpool, always came over to Plumstock on Friday evening, and spent Saturday and Sunday with the rector and his family. For him those Saturdays were happy days, for Frederic F. Frew was a good lover. He liked to be with Nora, to walk with her, and to talk with her. He liked to show her that he loved her, and to make himself gracious and pleasant. I am not so sure that his coming was equally agreeable to Mr Granger. Mr Frew would talk about American politics, praising the feeling and spirit of his countrymen in the North; whereas Mr Granger, when driven into the subject, was constrained to make a battle for the South. All his prejudices, and what he would have called his judgment, went with the South; and he was not ashamed of his opinion; but he disliked arguing with Frederic F. Frew. I fear it must be confessed that Frederic F. Frew was too strong for him in such arguments. Why it should be so I cannot say; but an American argues more closely on politics than does an Englishman. His convictions are not the truer on that account; very often the less true, as are the conclusions of a logician, because he trusts to syllogisms which are often false, instead of to the experience of his life and daily workings of his mind. But though not more true in his political convictions than an Englishman, he is more unanswerable, and therefore Mr Granger did not care to discuss the subject of the American war with Frederic F. Frew.

'It riles me,' Frew said, as he sat after dinner in the Plumstock drawing-room on the Friday evening before Christmas day, 'to hear your folks talking of our elections. They think the war will come to an end, and the rebels of the South will have their own way, because the Democrats have carried their ticket.'

'It will have that tendency,' said the parson.

'Not an inch; any more than your carrying the Reform

Bill or repealing the Corn Laws had a tendency to put down the throne. It's the same sort of argument. Your two parties were at daggers' drawn about the Reform Bill; but that did not cause you to split on all other matters.'

'But the throne wasn't in question,' said the parson.

'Nor is the war in question; not in that way. The most popular Democrat in the States at this moment is M'Clellan –'

'And they say no one is so anxious to see the war ended.'

'Whoever says so slanders him. If you don't trust his deeds, look at his words.'

'I believe in neither,' said the parson.

'Then put him aside as a nobody. But you can't do that, for he is the man whom the largest party in the Northern States trusts most implicitly. The fact is, sir' – and Frederic F. Frew gave the proper twang to the last letter of the last word – 'you, none of you here, understand our politics. You can't realize the blessings of a –'

'Molly, give me some tea,' said the rector, in a loud voice. When matters went as far as this he did not care by what means he stopped the voice of his future relative.

'All I say is this,' continued Frew, 'you will find out your mistake if you trust to the Democratic elections to put an end to the war, and bring cotton back to Liverpool.'

'And what is to put an end to the war?' asked Nora.

'Victory and union,' said Frederic F. Frew.

'Exhaustion,' said Charley from Oxford.

'Compromise,' said Bobby from Liverpool.

'The Lord Almighty, when he shall have done his work,' said the parson. 'And, in the meantime, Molly, do you keep plenty of fire under the kitchen boiler.'

That was clearly the business of the present hour for all in Mr Granger's part of the country; – we may say, indeed, for all on Mr Granger's side of the water. It mattered little, then, in Lancashire, whether New York might have a

43

Democratic or a Republican governor. The old cotton had been burned; the present crop could not be garnered; the future crop – the crop which never would be future, could not get itself sown. Mr Granger might be a slow politician, but he was a practical man, understanding the things immediately around him; and they all were aware – Frederic F. Frew with the rest of them – that he was right when he bade his wife keep the fire well hot beneath the kitchen boiler.

'Isn't it almost wicked to be married in such a time as this?' It was much later in the evening when Nora, still troubled in her mind about her widow's mite, whispered these words into her lover's ears. If she were to give up her lover for twelve months, would not that be a throwing in of something to the treasury from off her own back and out of her own mouth? But then this matter of her marriage had been so fully settled that she feared to think of disturbing it. He would never consent to such a post-ponement. And then the offering, to be of avail for her, must be taken from her own back, not from his; and Nora had an idea that in the making of such an offering as that suggested, Mr Frederic F. Frew would conceive that he had contributed by far the greater part. Her uncle called him an Amalekite, and she doubted whether it would be just to spoil an Amalekite after such a fashion as that. Nevertheless, into his ears she whispered her little proposition.

'Wicked to get married!' said Frederic. 'Not according to my idea of the Christian religion.'

'Oh! but you know what I mean;' and she gave his arm a slight caressing pinch. At this time her uncle had gone to his own room; her cousins had gone to their studies, – by which I believe they intended to signify the proper smoking of a pipe of tobacco in the rectory kitchen; and Mrs Granger, seated in her easy-chair, had gone to her slumbers, dreaming of the amount of fuel with which that kitchen boiler must be supplied.

'I shall bring a breach of promise against you,' said Frederic, 'if you don't appear in church with bridal array on Monday, the 12th of January, and pay the pounds into the war-treasury. That would be a spoiling of the Amalekite.' Then he got hold of the fingers which had pinched him.

'Of course I shan't put it off, unless you agree.'

'Of course you won't.'

'But, dear Fred, don't you think we ought?'

'No; certainly not. If I thought you were in earnest I would scold you.'

'I am in earnest – quite. You need not look in that way, for you know very well how truly I love you. You know I want to be your wife above all things.'

'Do you?' And then he began to insinuate his arm round her waist; but she got up and moved away, not as in anger at his caress, but as showing that the present moment was unfit for it.

'I do,' she said, 'above all things. I love you so well that I could hardly bear to see you go away again without taking me with you. I could hardly bear it, – but I could bear it.'

'Could you? Then I couldn't. I'm a weaker vessel than you, and your strength must give way to my weakness.'

'I know I've no right to tax you, – if you really care about it.' Frederic F. Frew made no answer to this in words, but pursued her in her retreat from the sofa on which they had sat.

'Don't, Fred. I am so much in earnest. I wish I knew what I ought to do to throw in my two mites.'

'Not throw me over certainly, and break all the promises you have made for the last twelve months. You can't be in earnest. It's out of the question, you know.'

'Oh! I am in earnest.'

'I never heard of such a thing in my life. What good

would it do? It wouldn't bring the cotton in. It wouldn't feed the poor. It wouldn't keep your aunt's boiler hot.'

'No; that it wouldn't,' said Mrs Granger, starting up; 'and coals are such a terrible price.' Then she went to sleep again, and ordered in large supplies in her dreams.

'But I should have done as much as the widow did. Indeed I should, Fred. Oh, dear! – to have to give you up! But I only meant for a year.'

'As you are so very fond of me' –

'Of course, I'm fond of you. Should I let you do like that if I was not?' At the moment of her speaking he had again got his arm round her waist.

'Then I'm too charitable to allow you to postpone your happiness for a day. We'll look at it in that way.'

'You won't understand me, or rather you do understand me, and pretend that you don't, which is very wrong.'

'I always was very wicked.'

'Then why don't you make yourself better? Do not you too wish to be a widow? You ought to wish it.'

'I should like to have an opportunity of trying married life first.'

'I won't stay any longer with you, sir, because you are scoffing. Aunt, I'm going to bed.' Then she returned again across the room, and whispered to her lover: 'I'll tell you what, sir; I'll marry you on Monday the 12th of January, if you'll take me just as I am now: with a bonnet on, and a shawl over my dress: exactly as I walked out with you before dinner. When I made the promise, I never said anything about fine clothes.'

'You may come in an old red cloak, if you like it.'

'Very well; now mind I've got your consent. Good-night, sir. After all it will only be half a mite.' She had turned towards the door, and had her hand upon the lock; but she came back into the room, close up to him. 'It will not be a quarter of a mite,' she said. 'How can it be anything if I get you?' Then she kissed him, and hurried away out of the room, before he could again speak to her.

'What, what, what!' said Mrs Granger, waking up. 'So Nora has gone, has she?'

'Gone; yes, just this minute,' said Frew, who had turned his face to the fire, so that the tear in his eyes might not be seen. As he took himself off to his bed, he swore to himself that Nora Field was a trump, and that he had done well in securing for himself such a wife; but it never occurred to him that she was in any way in earnest about her wedding dress. She was a trump because she was so expressive in her love to himself, and because her eyes shone so brightly when she spoke eagerly on any matter; but as to her appearing at the altar in a red cloak, or, as was more probable, in her own customary thick woollen shawl, he never thought about it. Of course she would be married as other girls are married.

Nor had Nora thought of it till that moment in which she made the proposition to her lover. As she had said before, her veil was ordered, and so was her white silk dress. Her bonnet also had been ordered, with its bridal wreath, and the other things assorting therewith. A vast hole was to be made in her grand-aunt's legacy for the payment of all this finery; but, as Mrs Granger had said to her, in so spending it, she would best please her future husband. He had enough of his own, and would not care that she should provide herself with articles which he could afterwards give her, at the expense of that little smartness at his wedding which an American likes, at any rate, as well as an Englishman. Nora, with an honesty which some ladies may not admire, had asked her lover the question in the plainest language. 'You will have to buy my things so much the sooner,' she had said. 'I'd buy them all to-morrow, only you'll not let me.' 'I should rather think not, Master Fred.' Then she had gone off with her aunt, and ordered her wedding-clothes. But now as she prepared for bed after the conversation which has just been recorded, she began to think in earnest whether it would not be well to dispense with white silk and orange wreaths while so many were dispensing with – were forced to dispense with bread and fuel. Could she bedizen herself with finery from Liverpool, while her uncle was, as she well knew, refusing himself a set of new shirts which he wanted sorely, in order that he might send to the fund at Liverpool the money which they would cost him? He was throwing in his two mites daily, as was her aunt, who toiled unceasingly at woollen shawls and woollen stockings, so that she went on knitting even in her sleep. But she, Nora, since the earnestness of these bad days began, had done little or nothing. Her needle, indeed, had been very busy, but it had been busy in preparation for Mr Frederic F. Frew's nuptials. Even Bob and Charley worked for the Relief Committee; but she had done nothing: nothing but given her two pounds. She had offered four, but her uncle, with a self-restraint never before or afterwards practised by him, had chucked her back two, saying that he would not be too hard even upon an Amalekite. As she thought of the word, she asked herself whether it was not more incumbent on her, than on anyone else, to do something in the way of self-sacrifice. She was now a Briton, but would shortly be an American. Should it be said of her that the distress of her own countrywomen, the countrywomen whom she was leaving, did not wring her heart? It was not without a pang that she prepared to give up that nationality, which all its owners rank as the first in the world, and all who do not own it, rank, if not as the first, then as the second. Now it seemed to her as though she were deserting her own family in its distress, deserting her own ship in the time of its storm, and she was going over to those from whom this distress and this storm had come! Was it not needful that she should do something; that she should satisfy herself that she had been willing to suffer in the cause?

She would throw in her two mites if she only knew where to find them. 'I could only do it in truth,' she said to herself, as she rose from her prayers, 'by throwing in him. I have got one very great treasure, but I have not got anything else that I care about. After all, it isn't so easy to be a widow with two mites.' Then she sat down and thought about it. As to postponing her marriage, that she knew to be in truth quite out of the question. Even if she could bring herself to do it, everybody about her would say that she was mad, and Mr Frederic F. Frew might not impossibly destroy himself with one of those pretty revolvers which he sometimes brought out from Liverpool for her to play with. But was it not practicable for her to give up her wedding-clothes? There would be considerable difficulty even in this. As to their having been ordered, that might be overcome by the sacrifice of some portion of the price. But then her aunt and even her uncle would oppose her; her cousins would cover her with ridicule – in the latter matter she might, however, achieve something of her widowhood; – and, after all, the loss would fall more upon F. F. Frew than upon herself. She really did not care for herself in what clothes she was married, so that she was made his wife. But as regarded him, might it not be disagreeable to him to stand before the altar with a dowdy creature in an old gown? And then there was one other consideration. Would it not seem that she was throwing in her two mites publicly before the eyes of all men, as a Pharisee might do it? Would there not be an ostentation in her widowhood? But as she continued to reflect, she cast this last thought behind her. It might be so said of her, but if such saying were untrue, if the offering were made in a widow's spirit, and not in the spirit of a Pharisee, would it not be cowardly to regard what men might say? Such false accusation would make some part of the two mites. 'I'll go into Liverpool about it on Monday,' she said to herself as she finally tucked the clothes around her.

Early in the following morning she was up and out of her room, with the view of seeing her aunt before she came down to breakfast; but the first person she met was her uncle. He accosted her in one of the passages. 'What, Nora, this is early for you! Are you going to have a morning lovers' walk with Frederic Franklin?'

'Frederic Franklin, as you choose to call him, uncle, never comes out of his room much before breakfast time. And it's raining hard.'

'Such a lover as he is ought not to mind rain.'

'But I should mind it, very much. But, uncle, I want to speak to you, very seriously. I have been making up my mind about something.'

'There's nothing wrong, is there, my dear?'

'No; there's nothing very wrong. It is not exactly about anything being wrong. I hardly know how to tell you what it is.' And then she paused, and he could see by the light of the candle in his hand that she blushed.

'Hadn't you better speak to your aunt?' said Mr Granger.

'That's what I meant to do when I got up,' said Nora; 'but as I have met you, if you don't mind – '

He assured her that he did not mind, and putting his hand upon her shoulder caressingly, promised her any assistance in his power. 'I'm not afraid that you will ask anything I ought not to do for you.'

Then she revealed to him her scheme, turning her face away from him as she spoke. 'It will be so horrid,' she said, 'to have a great box of finery coming home when you are all giving up everything for the poor people. And if you don't think it would be wrong – '

'It can't be wrong,' said her uncle. 'It may be a question of whether it would be wise.'

'I mean wrong to him. If it was to be any other clergyman, I should be ashamed of it. But as you are to marry us – '

'I don't think you need mind about the clergyman.'

'And of course I should tell the Foster girls.'

'The Foster girls?'

'Yes; they are to be my bridesmaids, and I am nearly sure they have not bought anything new yet. Of course they would think it all very dowdy, but I don't care a bit about it. I should just tell them that we had all made up our minds that we couldn't afford wedding-clothes. That would be true; wouldn't it?'

'But the question is about that wild American.'

'He isn't a wild American.'

'Well, then; about the tamed American. What will he say?'

'He said I might come in an old cloak.'

'You have told him, then?'

'But I'm afraid he thought I was only joking. But, uncle, if you'll help me, I think I can bring him round.'

'I daresay you can – to anything, just at present.'

'I didn't at all mean that. Indeed, I'm sure I couldn't bring him round to putting off the marriage.'

'No, no, no; not to that; to anything else.'

'I know you are laughing at me, but I don't much mind being laughed at. I should save very nearly fifteen pounds, if not quite. Think of that.'

'And you'd give it all to the soup-kitchen?'

'I'd give it all to you for the distress.'

Then her uncle spoke to her somewhat gravely. 'You're a good girl, Nora; a dear good girl. I think I understand your thoughts on this matter, and I love you for them. But I doubt whether there be any necessity for you to make this sacrifice. A marriage should be a gala festival according to the means of the people married, and the bridegroom has a right to expect that his bride shall come to him fairly arrayed, and bright with wedding trappings. I think we can do, my pet, without robbing you of your little braveries.'

'Oh, as for that, of course you can do without me.'

There was a little soreness in her tone; not because she was feeling herself to be misunderstood, but because she knew that she could not explain herself further. She could not tell her uncle that the poor among the Jews might have been relieved without the contribution of those two mites, but that the widow would have lost all had she not so contributed. She had hardly arranged her thoughts as to the double blessing of charity, and certainly could not express them with reference to her own case; but she felt the need of giving in this time of trouble something that she herself valued. She was right when she had said that it was hard to be a widow. How many among us, when we give, give from off our own backs, and from out of our own mouths? Who can say that he has sacrificed a want of his own; that he has abandoned a comfort; that he has worn a thread-bare coat, when coats with their gloss on have been his customary wear; that he has fared roughly on cold scraps, whereas a well-spread board has been his usual daily practice? He who has done so, has thrown in his two mites, and for him will charity produce her double blessing.

Nora thought that it was not well in her uncle to tell her that he could do without her wedding-clothes. Of course he could do without them. But she soon threw those words behind her, and went back upon the words which had preceded them: 'The bridegroom has a right to expect that the bride shall come to him fairly arrayed.' After all, that must depend upon circumstances. Suppose the bride had no means of arraying herself fairly without getting into debt; what would the bridegroom expect in that case? 'If he'll consent, you will?' she said, as she prepared to leave her uncle.

'You'll drive him to offer to pay for the things himself.'

'I daresay he will, and then he'll drive me to refuse. You may be quite sure of this, uncle, that whatever clothes I do wear, he will never see the bill of them'; and then that conference was ended.

'I've made that calculation again,' said Bob at breakfast, 'and I feel convinced that if an Act of Parliament could be passed restricting the consumption of food in Christmas week, the entire week, mind, to that of ordinary weeks, we should get two millions of money, and that those two millions would tide us over till the Indian cotton comes in. Of course I mean by food, butchers' meat, groceries, spirits, and wines. Only think, that by one measure, which would not entail any real disappointment on anyone, the whole thing would be done.'

'But the Act of Parliament wouldn't give us the money,' said his father.

'Of course I don't really mean an Act of Parliament; that would be absurd. But the people might give up their Christmas dinners.'

'A great many will, no doubt. Many of those most in earnest are pretty nearly giving up their daily dinners. Those who are indifferent will go on feasting the same as ever. You can't make a sacrifice obligatory.'

'It would be no sacrifice if you did,' said Nora, still thinking of her wedding-clothes.

'I doubt whether sacrifices ever do any real good,' said Frederic F. Frew.

'Oh, Fred!' said Nora.

'We have rather high authority as to the benefit of self-denial,' said the parson.

'A man who can't sacrifice himself must be selfish,' said Bobby; 'and we are all agreed to hate selfish people.'

'And what about the widow's mite?' said Mrs. Granger.

'That's all very well, and you may knock me down with the Bible if you like, as you might do also if I talked about pre-Adamite formations. I believe every word of the Bible, but I do not believe that I understand it all thoroughly.'

53

'You might understand it better if you studied it more,' said the parson.

'Very likely. I won't be so uncourteous as to say the same thing of my elders. But now, about these sacrifices. You wouldn't wish to keep people in distress that you might benefit yourself by releasing them?'

'But the people in distress are there,' said Nora.

'They oughtn't to be there; and as your self-sacrifices, after all, are very insufficient to prevent distress, there certainly seems to be a question open whether some other mode should not be tried. Give me the country in which the humanitarian principle is so exercised that no one shall be degraded by the receipt of charity. It seems to me that you like poor people here in England that you may gratify yourselves by giving them, not as much to eat as they want, but just enough to keep their skins from falling off their bones. Charity may have its double blessing, but it may also have its double curse.'

'Not charity, Mr Frew,' said Mrs Granger.

'Look at your Lady Bountifuls.'

'Of course it depends on the heart,' continued the lady; 'but charity, if it be charity' –

'I'll tell you what,' said Frederic F. Frew, interrupting her. 'In Philadelphia, which in some matters is the best organized city I know' –

'I'm going down to the village,' said the parson, jumping up; 'who is to come with me?' and he escaped out of the room before Frew had had an opportunity of saying a word further about Philadelphia.

'That's the way with your uncle always,' said he, turning to Nora, almost in anger. 'It certainly is the most conclusive argument I know – that of running away.'

'Mr Granger meant it to be conclusive,' said the elder lady.

'But the pity is that it never convinces.'

'Mr Granger probably had no desire of convincing.'

'Ah! Well, it does not signify,' said Frew. 'When a man has a pulpit of his own, why should he trouble himself to argue in any place where counter arguments must be met and sustained?'

Nora was almost angry with her lover, whom she regarded as stronger and more clever than any of her uncle's family, but tyrannical and sometimes overbearing in the use of his strength. One by one her aunt and cousins left the room, and she was left alone with him. He had taken up a newspaper as a refuge in his wrath, for in truth he did not like the manner in which his allusions to his own country were generally treated at the parsonage. There are Englishmen who think that every man differing with them is bound to bet with them on any point in dispute. 'Then you decline to back your opinion,' such men say when the bet is refused. The feeling of an American is the same as to those who are unwilling to argue with him. He considers that every intelligent being is bound to argue whenever matter of argument is offered to him; nor can he understand that any subject may be too sacred for argument. Frederic F. Frew, on the present occasion, was as a dog from whose very mouth a bone had been taken. He had given one or two loud, open growls, and now sat with his newspaper, showing his teeth as far as the spirit of the thing went. And it was in this humour that Nora found herself called upon to attack him on the question of her own proposed charity. She knew well that he could bark, even at her, if things went wrong with him. 'But then he never bites,' she said to herself. He had told her that she might come to her wedding in an old cloak if she pleased, but she had understood that there was nothing serious in this permission. Now, at this very moment, it was incumbent on her to open his eyes to the reality of her intention.

'Fred,' she said, 'are you reading that newspaper because you are angry with me?'

'I am reading the newspaper because I want to know what there is in it.'

'You know all that now, just as well as if you had written it. Put it down, sir!' And she put her hand on to the top of the sheet. 'If we are to be married in three weeks' time, I expect that you will be a little attentive to me now. You'll read as many papers as you like after that, no doubt.'

'Upon my word, Nora, I think your uncle is the most unfair man I ever met in my life.'

'Perhaps he thinks the same of you, and that will make it equal.'

'He can't think the same of me. I defy him to think that I'm unfair. There's nothing so unfair as hitting a blow, and then running away when the time comes for receiving the counterblow. It's what your Lord Chatham did, and he never ought to have been listened to in Parliament again.'

'That's a long time ago,' said Nora, who probably felt that her lover should not talk to her about Lord Chatham just three weeks before their marriage.

'I don't know that the time makes any difference.'

'Ah; – but I have got something else that I want to speak about. And, Fred, you mustn't turn up your nose at what we are all doing here, – as to giving away things, I mean.'

'I don't turn up my nose at it. Haven't I been begging of every American in Liverpool till I'm ashamed of myself?'

'I know you have been very good, and now you must be more good still, – good to me specially, I mean – That isn't being good. That's only being foolish.' What little ceremony had led to this last assertion I need not perhaps explain. 'Fred, I'm an Englishwoman to-day, but in a month's time I shall be an American.'

'I hope so, Nora, – heart and soul.'

'Yes, that is what I mean. Whatever is my husband's

country must be mine. And you know how well I love your country; do you not? I never run away when you talk to me about Philadelphia, – do I? And you know how I admire all your institutions – my institutions, as they will be.'

'Now, I know you're going to ask some very great favour.'

'Yes, I am; and I don't mean to be refused, Master Fred. I'm to be an American almost tomorrow, but as yet I am an Englishwoman, and I am bound to do what little I can before I leave my country. Don't you think so?'

'I don't quite understand.'

'Well, it's about my wedding-clothes. It does seem stupid talking about them, I know. But I want you to let me do without them altogether. Now you've got the plain truth. I want to give uncle Robert the money for his soup-kitchen, and to be married just as I am now. I do not care one straw what any other creature in the world may say about it, so long as I do not displease you.'

'I think it's nonsense, Nora.'

'Oh, Fred, don't say so. I have set my heart upon it. I'll do anything for you afterwards. Indeed, for the matter of that, I'd do anything on earth for you, whether you agree or whether you do not. You know that.'

'But, Nora, you wouldn't wish to make yourself appear foolish? How much money will you save?'

'Very nearly twenty pounds altogether.'

'Let me give you twenty pounds, so that you may leave it with your uncle by way of your two mites, as you call it.'

'No, no; certainly not. I might just as well send you the milliner's bill; might I not?'

'I don't see why you shouldn't do that.'

'Ah, but I do. You wouldn't wish me to be guilty of the pretence of giving a thing away, and then doing it out of your pocket. I have no doubt that what you are saying about the evil of promiscuous charity is quite true.' And then, as she flattered him with this wicked flattery, she looked up with her bright eyes into his face. 'But now, as the things are, we must be charitable, or the people will die. I feel almost like a rat leaving a falling house, in going away at this time; and if you would postpone it – '

'Nora!'

'Then I must be like a rat; but I won't be a rat in a white silk gown. Come now, say that you agree. I never asked you for anything before.'

'Everybody will think that you're mad, and that I'm mad, and that we are all mad together.'

'Because I go to church in a merino dress? Well; if that makes madness, let us be mad. Oh, Fred, do not refuse me the first thing I've asked you! What difference will it make? Nobody will know it over in Philadelphia!'

'Then you are ashamed of it?'

'No; not ashamed. Why should I be ashamed? But one does not wish to have that sort of thing talked about by everybody.'

'And you are so strong-minded, Nora, that you do not care about finery yourself?'

'Fred, that's ill-natured. You know very well what my feelings are. You are sharp enough to understand them without any further explanation. I do like finery; quite well enough, as you'll find out to your cost some day. And if ever you scold me – for extravagance, I shall tell you about this.'

'It's downright Quixotism.'

'Quixotism leads to nothing, but this will lead to twenty pounds' worth of soup; – and to something else too.'

When he pressed her to explain what that something else was, she declined to speak further on the subject. She could not tell him that the satisfaction she desired was that of giving up something, – of having made a sacrifice, – of having thrown into the treasury her two mites, – two mites off her own back, as she had said to her aunt, and out of her own mouth. He had taxed her with indifference to a woman's usual delight in gay plumage, and had taxed her most unjustly. 'He ought to know,' she said to herself, 'that I should not take all this trouble about it, unless I did care for it.' But, in truth, he did understand her motives thoroughly, and half approved them. He approved the spirit of self-abandonment, but disapproved the false political economy by which, according to his light, that spirit was accompanied. 'After all,' said he, 'the widow would have done better to have invested her small capital in some useful trade.'

'Oh, Fred, – but never mind now. I have your consent, and now I've only got to talk over my aunt.' So saying, she left her lover to turn over in his mind the first principles of that large question of charity.

'The giving of pence and halfpence, of scraps of bread and sups of soup is, after all, but the charity of a barbarous, half-civilized race. A dog would let another dog starve before he gave him a bone, and would see his starved fellow-dog die without a pang. We have just got beyond that, only beyond that, as long as we dole out sups of soup. But Charity, when it shall have made itself perfect, will have destroyed this little trade of giving, which makes the giver vain and the receiver humble. The Charity of the large-hearted is that which opens to every man the profit of his own industry; to every man and to every woman.' Then having gratified himself with the enunciation of this fine theory, he allowed his mind to run away to a smaller subject, and began to think of his own wedding garments. If Nora insisted on carrying out this project of hers, in what guise must he appear on the occasion? He also had ordered new clothes. 'It's just the sort of thing that they'll make a story of in Chestnut Street.' Chestnut Street, as we all know, is the West End of Philadelphia.

When the morning came of the twelfth of January, – the

morning that was to make Nora Field a married woman, she had carried her point; but she was not allowed to feel that she had carried it triumphantly. Her uncle had not forbidden her scheme, but had never encouraged it. Her lover had hardly spoken to her on the subject since the day on which she had explained to him her intention. 'After all, it's a mere bagatelle,' he had said; 'I am not going to marry your clothes.' One of her cousins, Bob, had approved; but he had coupled his approval with an intimation that something should be done to prevent any other woman from wearing bridal wreaths for the next three months. Charley had condemned her altogether, pointing out that it was bad policy to feed the cotton spinners at the expense of the milliners. But the strongest opposition had come from her aunt and the Miss Fosters. Mrs Granger, though her heart was in the battle which her husband was fighting, could not endure to think that all the time-honoured ceremonies of her life should be abandoned. In spite of all that was going on around her, she had insisted on having mince-pies on the table on Christmas-day. True, there were not many of them, and they were small and flavourless. But the mince-pies were there, with whisky to burn with them instead of brandy, if any of the party chose to go through the ceremony. And to her the idea of a wedding without wedding-clothes was very grievous. It was she who had told Nora that she was a widow with two mites, or might make herself one, if she chose to encounter self-sacrifice. But in so saying she had by no means anticipated such a widowhood as this. 'I really think, Nora, you might have one of those thinner silks, and you might do without a wreath; but you should have a veil, – indeed you should.' But Nora was obstinate. Having overcome her future lord, and quieted her uncle, she was not at all prepared to yield to the mild remonstrances of her aunt. The two Miss Fosters were very much shocked, and for three days there was a disagreeable coolness between them and the Plumstock family. A friend's bridal is always an occasion for a new dress, and the Miss Fosters naturally felt that they were being robbed of their rights.

'Sensible girl,' said old Foster, when he heard of it. 'When you're married, if ever you are, I hope you'll do the same.'

'Indeed we won't, papa,' said the two Miss Fosters. But the coolness gradually subsided, and the two Miss Fosters consented to attend in their ordinary Sunday bonnets.

It had been decided that they should be married early, at eight o'clock; that they should then go to the parsonage for breakfast, and that the married couple should start for London immediately afterwards. They were to remain there for a week, and then return to Liverpool for one other remaining week before their final departure for America. 'I should only have had them on for about an hour if I'd got them, and then it would have been almost dark,' she said to her aunt.

'Perhaps it won't signify very much,' her aunt replied. Then when the morning came, it seemed that the sacrifice had dwindled down to a very little thing. The two Miss Fosters had come to the parsonage overnight, and as they sat up with the bride over a bed-room fire, had been good-natured enough to declare that they thought it would be very good fun.

'You won't have to get up in the cold to dress me,' said Nora, 'because I can do it all myself; that will be one comfort.'

'Oh, we shouldn't have minded that; and as it is, of course, we'll turn you out nice. You'll wear one of your other new dresses; won't you?'

'Oh, I don't know, just what I'm to travel in. It isn't very old. Do you know after all I'm not sure that it isn't a great deal better.'

'I suppose it will be the same thing in the end,' said the

younger Miss Foster.

'Of course it will,' said the elder.

'And there won't be all that bother of changing my dress,' said Nora.

Frederic F. Frew came out to Plumstock by an early train, from Liverpool, bringing with him a countryman of his own as his friend on the occasion. It had been explained to the friend that he was to come in his usual habiliments.

'Oh, nonsense,' said the friend, 'I guess I'll see you turned off in a new waistcoat.' But Frederic F. Frew had made it understood that an old waistcoat was imperative.

'It's something about the cotton, you know. They're all beside themselves here, as though there was never going to be a bit more in the country to eat. That's England all over. Never mind; do you come just as if you were going into your counting-house. Brown cotton gloves, with a hole in the thumbs, will be the thing, I should say.'

There were candles on the table when they were all assembled in the parsonage drawing-room previous to the marriage. The two gentlemen were there first. Then came Mrs Granger, who rather frightened Mr Frew by kissing him, and telling him that she should always regard him as a son-in-law.

'Nora has always been like one of ourselves, you know,' she said, apologizingly.

'And let me tell you, Master Frew,' said the parson, 'that you're a very lucky fellow to get her.'

'I say, isn't it cold?' said Bob, coming in – 'where are the girls?'

'Here are the girls,' said Miss Foster, heading the procession of three which now entered the room, Nora, of course, being the last. Then Nora was kissed by everybody, including the strange American gentleman, who seemed to have made some mistake as to his privilege in the matter. But it all passed off very well, and I doubt if

Nora knew who kissed her. It was very cold, and they were all wrapped close in their brown shawls and greatcoats, and the women looked very snug and comfortable in their ordinary winter bonnets.

'Come,' said the parson, 'we mustn't wait for Charley; he'll follow us to church.' So the uncle took his niece on his arm, and the two Americans took the two bridesmaids, and Bob took his mother, and went along the beaten path over the snow to the church, and, as they got to the door, Charley rushed after them quite out of breath.

'I haven't even got a pair of gloves at all,' he whispered to his mother.

'It doesn't matter; nobody's to know,' said Mrs Granger.

Nora by this time had forgotten the subject of her dress altogether, and it may be doubted if even the Misses Foster were as keenly alive to it as they thought they would have been. For myself, I think they all looked more comfortable on that cold winter morning without the finery which would have been customary than they could have done with it. It had seemed to them all beforehand that a marriage without veils and wreaths, without white gloves and new gay dresses, would be but a *triste* affair; but the idea passed away altogether when the occasion came. Mr Granger and his wife and the two lads clustered round Nora as they made themselves ready for the ceremony, uttering words of warm love, and it seemed as though even the clerk and the servants took nothing amiss. Frederic F. Frew had met with a rebuff in the hall of the parsonage, in being forbidden to take his own bride under his own arm; but when the time for action came, he bore no malice, but went through his work manfully. On the whole, it was a pleasant wedding, homely, affectionate, full of much loving greeting; not without many sobs on the part of the bride and of Mrs Granger, and some slight suspicion of an eagerly-removed tear in the parson's eye; but this, at any rate, was certain, that the wedding-clothes were not missed. When they all sat down to their breakfast in the parsonage dining-room, that little matter had come to be clean forgotten. No one knew, not even the Misses Foster, that there was anything at all extraordinary in their garb. Indeed, as to all gay apparel, we may say that we only miss it by comparison. It is very sad to be the wearer of the only frock-coat in company, to carry the one solitary black silk handkerchief at a dinner party. But I do not know but that a dozen men so arrayed do not seem to be as well dressed as though they had obeyed the latest rules of fashion as to their garments. One thing, however, had been made secure. That sum of twenty pounds, saved from the milliners, had been duly paid over into Mr. Granger's hands.

'It has been all very nice,' said Mrs. Granger, still sobbing, when Nora went upstairs to tie on her bonnet before she started. 'Only you are going!'

'Yes, I'm going now, aunt. Dear aunt! But, aunt, I have failed in one thing – absolutely failed.'

'Failed in what, my darling?'

'There has been no widow's mite. It is not easy to be a widow with two mites.'

'What you have given will be blessed to you, and blessed to those who will receive it.'

'I hope it may; but I almost feel that I have been wrong in thinking of it so much. It has cost me nothing. I tell you, aunt, that it is not easy to be a widow with two mites.'

When Mrs Granger was alone with her husband after this, the two Miss Fosters having returned to Liverpool under the discreet protection of the two younger Grangers, for they had positively refused to travel with no other companion than the strange American – she told him all that Nora had said. 'And who can tell us,' he replied, 'that it was not the same with the widow herself? She threw in all that she had, but who can say that she suffered aught in consequence? It is my belief that all that is given in a right spirit comes back instantly, in this world, with interest.'

'I wish my coals would come back,' said Mrs Granger.

'Perhaps you have not given them in a right spirit, my dear.'

Poetry

The Oxen

Christmas Eve, and twelve of the clock.
'Now they are all on their knees,'
An elder said as we sat in a flock
By the embers in hearthside ease.

We pictured the meek mild creatures where
They dwelt in their strawy pen,
Nor did it occur to one of us there
To doubt they were kneeling then.

So fair a fancy few would weave
In these years! Yet, I feel,
If someone said on Christmas Eve,
'Come; see the oxen kneel

'In the lonely barton by yonder coomb
Our childhood used to know,'
I should go with him in the gloom,
Hoping it might be so.

THOMAS HARDY

Christmas is really for the children

Christmas is really
for the children.
Especially for children
who like animals, stables,
stars and babies wrapped
in swaddling clothes.
Then there are wise men,
kings in fine robes,
humble shepherds and a
hint of rich perfume.

Easter is not really
for the children
unless accompanied by
a cream filled egg.
It has whips, blood, nails,
a spear and allegations
of body snatching.
It involves politics, God
and the sins of the world.
It is not good for people
of a nervous disposition.
They would do better to
think on rabbits, chickens
and the first snowdrop
of spring.

Or they'd do better to
wait for a re-run of
Christmas without asking
too many questions about
what Jesus did when he grew up
or whether there's any connection.

STEVE TURNER

Magi

Wintering swans shake out their heavy robes.
Instinct as sure as a star has led them
across a frozen desert of sky

to pinpoint in ice-locked washes among
trapped reeds, this small epiphany of water.
We follow their huge soft prints in the snow.

Below the wooden hide they bow their heads.
They drink. Their ripples nudge the doubting ice.
We watch for the white feathers of a thaw.

EMMA DANES

Carol

I sing of a maiden
   That is makeles;
King of all kings
   To her son she ches.

He came al so still
   There his mother was,
As dew in April
   That falleth on the grass.

He came al so still
   To his mother's bour,
As dew in April
   That falleth on the flour.

He came al so still
   There his mother lay,
As dew in April
   That falleth on the spray.

Mother and maiden
   Was never none but she;
Well may such a lady
   Goddes mother be.

makeles: matchless
ches: chose
flour: flower

ANONYMOUS
15th century

A Christmas Carol

In the bleak mid-winter
   Frosty wind made moan,
Earth stood hard as iron,
   Water like a stone;
Snow had fallen, snow on snow,
   Snow on snow,
In the bleak mid-winter
   Long ago.

Our God, Heaven cannot hold Him
   Nor earth sustain;
Heaven and earth shall flee away
   When He comes to reign:
In the bleak mid-winter
   A stable-place sufficed
The Lord God Almighty
   Jesus Christ.

Enough for Him whom cherubim
   Worship night and day,
A breastful of milk
   And a mangerful of hay;
Enough for Him whom angels
   Fall down before,
The ox and ass and camel
   Which adore.

Angels and archangels
　　May have gathered there,
Cherubim and seraphim
　　Throng'd the air,
But only His mother
　　In her maiden bliss
Worshipped her Beloved
　　With a kiss.

What can I give Him,
　　Poor as I am?
If I were a shepherd
　　I would bring a lamb,
If I were a wise man
　　I would do my part; –
Yet what I can I give Him,
　　Give my heart.

CHRISTINA ROSSETTI

From *Hamlet*

MARCELLUS: Some say that ever 'gainst that season comes
Wherein our Saviour's birth is celebrated,
The bird of dawning singeth all night long;
And then, they say, no spirit dare stir abroad;
The nights are wholesome; then no planets strike,
No fairy takes, nor witch hath power to charm;
So hallow'd and so gracious is the time.

HORATIO: So have I heard, and do in part believe it.

SHAKESPEARE

Feast of the Annunciation

Herself a rose, who bore the Rose,
She bore the Rose and felt its thorn.
All Loveliness new-born
Took on her bosom its repose,
And slept and woke there night and morn.

Lily herself, she bore the one
Fair Lily; sweeter, whiter, far
Than she or others are:
The Sun of Righteousness her Son,
She was His morning star.

She gracious, He essential Grace,
He was the Fountain, she the rill:
Her goodness to fulfil
And gladness, with proportioned pace
He led her steps thro' good and ill.

Christ's mirror she of grace and love,
Of beauty and of life and death:
By hope and love and faith
Transfigured to His Likeness, 'Dove,
Spouse, Sister, Mother,' Jesus saith.

CHRISTINA ROSSETTI

The Nativity of Christ

Behold the Father is his daughter's son,
The bird that built the nest is hatched therein,
The old of years an hour hath not outrun,
Eternal life to live doth now begin,
The Word is dumb, the mirth of heaven doth weep,
Might feeble is, and force doth faintly creep.

O dying souls, behold your living spring;
O dazzled eyes, behold your sun of grace;
Dull ears, attend what word this Word doth bring;
Up, heavy hearts, with joy your joy embrace.
From death, from dark, from deafness, from despairs,
This life, this light, this Word, this joy repairs.

Gift better than himself God doth not know;
Gift better than his God no man can see.
This gift doth here the giver given bestow;
Gift to this gift let each receiver be.
God is my gift, himself he freely gave me;
God's gift am I, and none but God shall have me.

Man altered was by sin from man to beast;
Beast's food is hay, hay is all mortal flesh.
Now God is flesh and lies in manger pressed
As hay, the brutest sinner to refresh.
O happy field wherein this fodder grew,
Whose taste doth us from beasts to men renew.

ROBERT SOUTHWELL

Minstrels

The minstrels played their Christmas tune
To-night beneath my cottage-eaves;
While, smitten by a lofty moon,
The encircling laurels, thick with leaves,
Gave back a rich and dazzling sheen,
That overpowered their natural green.

Through hill and valley every breeze
Had sunk to rest with folded wings:
Keen was the air, but could not freeze,
Nor check, the music of the strings;
So stout and hardy were the band
That scraped the chords with strenuous hand.

And who but listened? – till was paid
Respect to every inmate's claim,
The greeting given, the music played
In honour of each household name,
Duly pronounced with lusty call,
And 'Merry Christmas' wished to all.

WILLIAM WORDSWORTH

Lullay, lullay, little child

Lullay, lullay, little child,
Thou that were so stern and wild,
Now art becomen meek and mild,
    To save that was forlore.

But for my sin I wot it is
That Goddēs son suffered this;
Mercy, Lord! I have done miss,
    Iwis I will no more.

Against my Father's will I ches
An apple with a rueful res;
Wherefore mine heritage I les
    And now thou weepest therefore.

An apple I took of a tree
God it had forbidden me:
Wherefore I should damnèd be,
    If thy weeping ne wore.

Lullay for woe, thou little thing,
Thou little baron, thou little king;
Mankind is cause of thy mourning,
    That thou hast lovèd so yore.

For man that thou hast ay loved so
Yet shalt thou suffer painēs mo,
In head, in feet, in handēs too,
    And yet weepen well more.

That pain us make of sinnē free,
That pain us bring, Jesu, to thee,
That pain us help ay to flee,
    The wicked fiendēs lore. Amen.

wot: know
Iwis: certainly
ches: chose
les: lost
If thy weeping ne wore: were it not for thy weeping
so yore: so long
ay: ever

ANONYMOUS
14th century

The Skating Minister

(after a painting by Raeburn)

A clergyman skates from Christmas to Easter
on Duddingston Loch. In the dusty nave
of hills and mist he engraves his sermon –
a birth, a death – loops and ellipses till
the end can't be told from the beginning.

He makes it look easy, leans forward as from
the pulpit, flushed, in his stride. Already
light tears at a veil of cloud. He senses
new life running just under the ice, etches
its current in swift, irrefutable curves.

EMMA DANES

Christmastide

Love came down at Christmas,
Love all lovely, Love Divine;
Love was born at Christmas,
Star and Angels gave the sign.

Worship we the Godhead,
Love Incarnate, Love Divine;
Worship we our Jesus:
But wherewith for sacred sign?

Love shall be our token,
Love be yours and love be mine,
Love to God and all men,
Love for plea and gift and sign.

CHRISTINA ROSSETTI

The May Magnificat

May is Mary's month, and I
Muse at that and wonder why:
 Her feasts follow reason,
 Dated due to season –

Candlemas, Lady Day,
But the Lady Month, May,
 Why fasten that upon her,
 With a feasting in her honour?

Is it only its being brighter
Than the most are must delight her?
 Is it opportunest
 And flowers finds soonest?

Ask of her, the mighty mother:
Her reply puts this other
 Question: What is Spring? –
 Growth in every thing –

Flesh and fleece, fur and feather,
Grass and greenworld all together;
 Star-eyed strawberry-breasted
 Throstle above her nested

Cluster of bugle blue eggs thin
Forms and warms the life within;
 And bird and blossom swell
 In sod or sheath or shell.

All things rising, all things sizing
Mary sees, sympathizing
   With that world of good,
   Nature's motherhood.

Their magnifying of each its kind
With delight calls to mind
   How she did in her stored
   Magnify the Lord.

Well but there was more than this:
Spring's universal bliss
   Much, had much to say
   To offering Mary May.

When drop-of-blood-and-foam-dapple
Bloom lights the orchard-apple
   And thicket and thorp are merry
   With silver surfed cherry

And azuring-over greybell makes
Wood banks and brakes wash wet like lakes
   And magic cuckoocall
   Caps, clears, and clinches all –

This ecstasy all through mothering earth
Tells Mary her mirth till Christ's birth
   To remember and exultation
   In God who was her salvation.

GERARD MANLEY HOPKINS

The Christmas Goose

William Topaz McGonagall (1825 – 1902) is widely regarded as the worst poet in the world.
Here is an example of his work.

Mr Smiggs was a gentleman,
And he lived in London town;
His wife she was a good kind soul,
And seldom known to frown.

'Twas on Christmas eve,
And Smiggs and his wife lay cosy in bed,
When the thought of buying a goose
Came into his head.

So the next morning,
Just as the sun rose,
He jump'd out of bed,
And he donn'd his clothes,

Saying, 'Peggy, my dear.
You need not frown,
For I'll buy you the best goose
In all London town.'

So away to the poultry shop he goes,
And bought the goose, as he did propose,
And for it he paid one crown,
The finest, he thought, in London town.

When Smiggs bought the goose
He suspected no harm,
But a naughty boy stole it
From under his arm.

Then Smiggs he cried, 'Stop, thief!
Come back with my goose!'
But the naughty boy laugh'd at him,
And gave him much abuse.

But a policeman captur'd the naughty boy,
And gave the goose to Smiggs,
And said he was greatly bother'd
By a set of juvenile prigs.

So the naughty boy was put in prison
For stealing the goose,
And got ten days' confinement
Before he got loose.

So Smiggs ran home to his dear Peggy,
Saying, 'Hurry, and get this fat goose ready,
That I have bought for one crown;
So, my darling, you need not frown.'

'Dear Mr Smiggs, I will not frown:
I'm sure 'tis cheap for one crown,
Especially at Christmas time –
Oh! Mr Smiggs, it's really fine.'

'Peggy, it is Christmas time,
So let us drive dull care away,
For we have got a Christmas goose,
So cook it well, I pray.

'No matter how the poor are clothed,
Or if they starve at home,
We'll drink our wine, and eat our goose,
Aye, and pick it to the bone.'

WILLIAM MCGONAGALL

From
St John's Gospel

The Word was in the beginning.

The Word was with God;
The Word was God.
He was with God in the beginning.

Through him, everything was created;
Nothing was created without him.

Life was in him;
The Life was humanity's Light.
The Light shines in the darkness;
The darkness has not grasped it.

A man named John was sent from God.
He came as a witness,
To witness to the Light,
So that everyone might believe by him.

(He was not the Light;
He came to witness to the Light.)

It was the true Light
Who enlightens everyone
Who was coming into the world.

He was in the world;
The world was created through him –
But the world did not know him.

He came to his own;
His own did not accept him.

Yet to those who accepted him
He gave the authority to become children of God –
To those who had faith in his name.
They became his children,
Not because of their blood,
Nor from mortal desire,
Nor from human will:
It was God who made them his children.

The Word became flesh;
He pitched his tent among us.

We have seen the Word's majesty;
The majesty of the Father's only Son,
Full of grace and truth.

(John witnessed to him: he proclaimed,
'This is he of whom I said,
"He who comes after me is before me:
It is, indeed, he who was first.' ")

From his abundance, all of us have received
Grace upon grace.

Through Moses, the Torah was given;
Through Jesus Christ, grace and truth came.

No-one has seen God,
Yet the only Son, who belongs to the Father's very being –
He showed us what God is.

TRANSLATED FROM THE GREEK BY DAVID BARNES

Note: 'The Word' translates the Greek term *Logos*. The Stoic school of philosophy used it when they talked about God. John also uses it because it related to the Word of God in the Old Testament, which was heard by the prophets. The Logos, then, means God's self-communication, his communication of himself.

The darkness has not grasped it: the Greek for 'grasped' means both 'understood' and 'laid hands on' or 'defeated'. The English word 'grasped' conveys both senses.

Pitched his tent among among us: this is a more accurate translation than the usual 'dwelt among us'; the word John uses is quite specific.

Lord, Lord

You were hungry
and I was sorry.
You were thirsty
and I blamed the world.
You were a stranger
and I pointed you out.
You were naked
and I turned you in.
You were sick
and I said a prayer.
You were in prison
and I wrote a poem.

STEVE TURNER

Miscellany

Christmas Day

The word 'Christmas' comes from the Old English *Cristes Maesse* ('Christ's Mass').

Jesus was probably born in 4 BC. 7 BC is sometimes suggested but 4 is more likely. The Anno Domini system was worked out in the sixth century by a monk called Dionysius Exiguus – and he got his sums wrong. (So, to find out what the current year should be, add four to today's date. Or seven. But four's more likely.) If we go for 4 BC, Jesus would have been between 33 and 37 when he died; perhaps a little older than is often thought.

(The date of the crucifixion is 29, 30 or 33 AD; it's impossible to be sure which.)

Dionysius' method of dating made the year of Jesus' birth 1 AD. There isn't, or wasn't, a year zero. The year before 1 AD is 1 BC.

The earliest Church did not have a feast to celebrate the birth of Christ. The Christian theologian Clement of Alexandria (c. 150 - c. 215) recorded that some Egyptian Christians said Jesus was born on 20th May. Epiphanius, a fourth century Christian writer, said Jesus was born on 6th January.

It's often said that the Christians hit upon the date of 25th December because that was the festival of Sol Invictus and they wanted to Christianise it. Actually, this isn't certain. It's true that 25th December was kept as the festival of Sol Invictus: *the Invincible* or *Unconquered Sun* in English; the cult of this Syrian god was given the official stamp of approval by the Emperor Aurelian in 274. The idea is that the Invincible Sun is replaced by the the Sun of Justice, or the Sun of Righteousness – a phrase from Malachi 4.2 in the Old Testament, later applied to Jesus.

There's another theory. In the third century, Christians generally took the view that John the Baptist was conceived on the autumn equinox. This would mean he was born on 25th June. Luke's Gospel says Jesus was conceived six months after John, so he must have been conceived at the spring equinox. That would place his birth on 25th December. (Third century Christians seemed very confident that babies would always arrive on their due date!)

Perhaps both theories together explain why December 25th was chosen. The calculations gave that as the date, and there was the bonus of Christianising a pagan festival. It was celebrated then by 336 in Rome, so by the fourth century, Christmas Day was fixed at 25th December.

There is, though, a calendrical difference. What we would normally call 25th December is the date according to the Gregorian calendar (so called because it was proposed by Pope Gregory XIII in 1582). The Gregorian calendar is the one that's now almost universally followed.

However, the Julian calendar, which is older, is still followed by Orthodox Christians for their feast days – or at least by the Orthodox in Russia, Serbia, Jerusalem and Georgia. 25th December on the Julian calendar is 7th January on the Gregorian one.

So, Christmas Day for these Orthodox Christians falls on 7th January.

The Orthodox Churches in Greece, Cyprus, Alexandria, Antioch, Romania, Bulgaria and Constantinople revised their calendars and celebrate Christmas Day on 25th December.

Numbers vary because nobody's counted them all, but it's estimated that 10,000,000 turkeys, 25,000,000 Christmas puddings and 35,000,000 bottles of wine are consumed in the UK at Christmas.

Fifteen facts about Father Christmas

1. The depiction of Father Christmas as a fat, bearded, jolly old man was standardised by the German-born American artist Thomas Nast (1840 – 1902). His cartoon of Father Christmas appeared in *Harper's Weekly* in January 1863. However, circumferential challenge and follicular prodigality pre-date Nash in pictures of Father Christmas.
2. The Coca-Cola Company did use Father Christmas for an advertising campaign in the 1930s, but it's a myth to say the red and white robes were invented by them because they're the Coca-Cola colours. In fact, red and white were used for him before; their adverts simply helped to fix them as Santa's standard livery. Before then, he was depicted wearing a variety of colours. Green was one of the more common ones.
3. 'Santa Claus' is an Americanisation of the Dutch 'Sinterklaas' or St Nicholas.
4. St Nicholas himself was the bishop of Myra in Lycia, which is now in Turkey. He was famous for giving gifts

to the poor.

5. Another figure behind the Father Christmas myth may be the Norse god Odin, who was said to fly through the sky with his hunting party. Children would leave out carrots or sugar for Odin's magical flying horse and, to thank them for their generosity, Odin would leave them sweets or presents in return. Some of the ideas about Odin may have survived among Germanic peoples and have then been Christianised and incorporated into the figure of St Nicholas.

6. The 1823 poem *The Night Before Christmas* fixed the following attributes in the popular imagination: the sledge that lands on the roof, squeezing down the chimney, and the names of the reindeer: Dasher, Dancer, Prancer, Vixen, Comet, Cupid, Dunder and Blixem (later amended to Donner and Blitzen).

7. Rudolph was not introduced until 1939 in a children's book by Robert L. May called – wait for it – *Rudolph the Red-Nosed Reindeer*. The red nose was not a consequence of Christmas excess but acted as a headlight to guide the sleigh through the night.

8. St Nicholas in legend dropped coins down the chimney of a poor person's house when he couldn't get them in any other way.

9. The world record for the largest number of people gathering in one place, dressed as Father Christmas, was established on 9th September 2007 in Derry. 12,965 people were so attired (or dressed as one of his helpers, which was deemed to count).

10. Father Christmas's address varies. In Canada, the address is: Santa Claus, North Pole, Canada H0H 0H0. The full address to write to him from the UK is Santa Claus, Reindeer Land, SAN TA1. In Finland, his address is Santa Claus' Main Post Office, Santa's Workshop Village, FIN-96930, Arctic Circle.

11. The number of snail mail communications to Father

Christmas still exceeds the number of emails.

12. Sherry and mince pies are not Father ᴄ universal snack of choice. In Sweden, rice porriᴏ out for him; in Ireland, Guinness (or milk) repla sherry. In the US and Canada, cookies and milk are ᴍore common.

13. In order to deliver all his presents, it has been calculated that Father Christmas could not spend more than 0.00008 seconds in each house. (Estimates vary.)

14. To carry all the toys, it has been estimated that the sleigh would have to weigh around 300,000 tons.

15. However, he would also have to travel so fast that he would vaporise due to the air resistance.

Good King Wenceslas

Good King Wenceslas did not look out on the Feast of Stephen. This was made up by the carol's writer, J. M. Neale. The real Wenceslas, or Wenzel, was Duke of Bohemia from 922 to 929 AD. He was a devout Christian (so J. M. Neale got that right) but this angered some of the pagan Bohemians, who duly murdered him on his way to church. He was only 22. His brother, Boleslav the Cruel, may have been mixed up in the murder, but Boleslav wanted to appear to be doing the right thing and moved Wenceslas' remains to the church of St Vitus in Prague. They became a centre for pilgrimage and Wenceslas became patron saint of Bohemia and later of the Czech Republic. His feast day, September 28th, is now Czech Statehood Day and is a public holiday.

In 2010, a survey was carried out of 5,363 different Christmas cards sold in supermarkets. Of these, 45 depicted the Christmas story: about 0.8% in total.

Christmas tree facts

It's often thought that Prince Albert is responsible for introducing the Christmas tree to the UK. It's true that he popularised them after bringing one over in 1841, but Christmas trees in this country are earlier. There's a record of a candlelit tree being set up in a street in London as early as the fifteenth century.

Christmas trees take about seven years to grow to a decent size and around six and a half million of them are sold in the UK every year.

The Christmas tree in Trafalgar Square is an annual gift from the people of Norway, to thank the UK for its help during the Second World War.

A survey by Debenhams in 2010 revealed that 80% of the UK's Christmas presents are bought by women.

The Royal Christmas Message

The first royal Christmas message was broadcast by King George V in 1932. The script was written by Rudyard Kipling.

The first to be televised was in 1957. Queen Elizabeth II has broadcast every year from 1952 to the present, with one exception. This was in 1969, when there was a scheduling clash: a documentary about the royal family had already been booked in for the slot and the Queen felt she had received enough television coverage that year.

Edward VIII never delivered a Christmas message. His reign lasted less than a year and he abdicated in early December 1936. George VI's first Christmas message was in 1937.

The 2006 message was the first to be available as a podcast and the 2008 one was the first in high definition.

Christmas cards

The first Christmas cards were produced by Sir Henry Cole in 1843, which was also the year Dickens wrote *A Christmas Carol*. They showed a jolly family drinking wine together, with the caption 'A merry Christmas and a happy new year to you'. (Cards with secular themes are not, then, a modern invention.) 2050 cards were printed and they cost a shilling. They're now worth rather more: one was sold in 2001 for £22,000.

The latest figures available from the Greeting Card Association are for 2008: 678 million cards were sold in the UK that year, with a total value of £267 million. They estimate that around £50 million annually is raised for charities by charity Christmas cards.

Another notable fact: in the UK, the Charities Advisory Trust grants the annual Scrooge Award. This goes to the charity Christmas cards which give the lowest percentage to the charities they 'support'.

The first Christmas stamps were not issued in the UK until 1964. The Postmaster General, one Tony Benn, thought it would be fun to have a competition to design them. The winners were Tazveer Shemza with 'King Wenceslas', and 'Snowman' by James Berry. Both artists were aged 6.

17 billion Christmas stamps have been printed in the UK since their introduction.

The Royal Mail first exhorted people to post early for Christmas in 1881.

You will no doubt be astonished to learn that most British people eat too much on Christmas Day: around 3000 calories more than is required. This means that on Christmas Day alone, you're liable to gain just under a pound in weight.

Boxing Day

Why St Stephen's Day is also called Boxing Day isn't certain. It clearly has something to do with opening boxes. Here are some explanations:

1. Metal boxes were placed outside churches for collections for the poor on St Stephen's Day.
2. Tradesmen collected their 'Christmas boxes' from the great and the good on Boxing Day.
3. Landowners gave their servants the day off so they could visit their families. They were given a box of gifts and cash.
4. It was the time when lords gave their serfs their allowance of tools, cloth and so on for the coming year. These were placed in boxes to make them easier to carry to the far parts of the estate.
5. Poor boxes in church were opened on Christmas Day, and the money was handed out on St Stephen's Day.

Whatever the origin, something that these explanations have in common is the idea of an obligation on the fortunate to look after the needs of those less fortunate.

In 1213, King John ordered 3000 capons, 1000 eels, 400 pigs, 100 lbs of almonds and 24 casks of wine for his Christmas dinner. (He presumably had other people to help him eat it.)

Twenty-Five Christmas Superstitions

1. People who are born on Christmas Day are lucky: they cannot be drowned or hanged.
2. People who are born on Christmas Day are unlucky: they have the ability to see ghosts and spooks.
3. People who are born on Christmas Eve turn into ghosts every Christmas Eve, while they're asleep. (That it only happens while they are asleep presumably explains why they don't remember it.)
4. Myrrh only blossoms on Christmas Eve.
5. And on Christmas Eve you can hear the bells of churches that have been submerged by seawater or floods, too.
6. The first person to hear the cock crow on Christmas Day will receive good luck.
7. Eat a fish at Christmas. Carry the scale in your pocket. Then you will never run out of money.

8. Alternatively, place said fish scale under your plate during Christmas dinner and good luck will be a certainty.

9. Wish someone a merry Christmas on Christmas morning *before* (not after) you put on your shoes and socks. You will then have good luck.

10. The same result can be achieved that day by kissing the oldest person in the house.

11. Or by sneezing.

12. Or by stirring the Christmas pudding.

13. Never, ever carry a spinning wheel from one side of the house to another on Christmas Day. It will ensure you bad luck.

14. So will not doing the washing up on Christmas Day.

15. Or getting shoes as a present.

16. Or turning a mattress.

17. If Christmas Day is a Thursday, the following year will be windy.

18. Everything that you dream about (when you're asleep) during Christmas will come true the following year. (This may be problematic for people who dream about tyrannosauruses playing the bagpipes or similar surreal things.)

19. A full moon on Christmas Day means next year's harvest will be bad.

20. If you're an unmarried woman and you whack a young pig with a stick on Christmas Day, you will marry a young husband.

21. It is bad luck to keep your decorations up after twelfth night.

22. On Christmas Eve, sit round the fire. Then look at your shadows. If your shadow has no head, it means you are going to die within twelve months.

23. On 27th December, do not eat meat. This will ensure you never catch fever.

24. If you let the fire go out on Christmas morning, spooks will come and plague you.

25. If your dog howls on Christmas Eve, it will go mad within the year.

Editor's note: Readers are advised that superstitions are very silly and must not be taken seriously.

Extract from Samuel Pepys' diary

Samuel Pepys (1633 - 1703) was the Chief Secretary to the Admiralty under Charles II and James II. He is also one of the most famous British diarists.
This extract comes from 1662. Pepys was then 29 years old.

Thursday 25 December 1662

(Christmas Day). Up pretty early, leaving my wife not well in bed, and with my boy walked, it being a most brave cold and dry frosty morning, and had a pleasant walk to White Hall, where I intended to have received the Communion with the family, but I came a little too late. So I walked up into the house and spent my time looking over pictures, particularly the ships in King Henry the VIIIth's Voyage to Bullen; marking the great difference between their build then and now. By and by down to the chappell again where Bishopp Morley preached upon the song of the Angels, 'Glory to God on high, on earth peace, and good will towards men.' Methought he made but a poor sermon, but long, and reprehending the mistaken jollity of the Court for the true joy that shall and ought to be on these days, he particularized concerning their excess in plays and gaming, saying that he whose office it is to keep the gamesters in order and within bounds, serves but for a second rather in a duell, meaning the groom-porter. Upon which it was worth observing how far they are come from taking the reprehensions of a bishopp seriously, that they all laugh in the chappell when he reflected on their ill actions and courses. He did much press us to joy in these publique days of joy, and to hospitality. But one that stood by whispered in my ear that the Bishopp himself do not spend one groat to the poor himself. The sermon done, a good anthem followed, with vialls, and then the King came down to receive the Sacrament. But I staid not, but calling my boy from my Lord's lodgings, and giving Sarah some good advice, by my Lord's order, to be sober and look after the house, I walked home again with great pleasure, and there dined by my wife's bed-side with great content, having a mess of brave plum-porridge and a roasted pullet for dinner, and I sent for a mince-pie abroad, my wife not being well to make any herself yet. After dinner sat talking a good while with her, her [pain] being become less, and then to see Sir W. Pen a little, and so to my office, practising arithmetique alone and making an end of last night's book with great content till eleven at night, and so home to supper and to bed.

Mince pies

Pies for Christmas have a long history in the UK, going back over 800 years. The recipe has varied; so has the name.   Until Victorian times, mince pies generally contained mutton, goose, beef or veal; traditionally, thirteen ingredients were used, perhaps symbolising Jesus and the twelve disciples. They were also called Christmas pies, shrid pies, minched pies or mutton pies and, again until the Victorian era, were much larger than they are today. They were also rectangular; the seventeenth century writer John Selden thought that the shape recalled the manger for the infant Jesus.

Whatever other ingredients were used, they seem to have always been heavily spiced. This may have resulted from the crusaders' bringing back with them recipe ideas from the Middle East. John Timbs, a Victorian antiquary, thought the spices symbolised the gifts brought by the Magi.

There's a sixteenth century tradition that you'll ensure good luck for twelve months if you eat a mince pie on each of the twelve days of Christmas.

Mince pies have been the object of suspicion from some non-conformist Christians, who thought them idolatrous. The Puritans famously banned them. A similar attitude is witnessed in an article *The Gentleman's Magazine* of 1733, which notes how some non-conformists 'inveigh against Christmas Pye, as an Invention of the Scarlet Whore of *Babylon,* an Hodge-Podge of Superstition, Popery, the Devil and all his Works.'

People who work on Christmas Day

On Christmas Day 2010, just under a million people went out to work in the UK. The Office for National

Statistics noted that a third of the total of 881,000 were health professionals (care assistants, nursing auxiliaries and nurses); 28,000 were cooks; 27,000 were security guards and 25,000 were police officers. About a third of all paramedics, midwives and farm managers had to work, though 43% of the clergy didn't. (The Office for National Statistics suggested this is because not all of them considered leading worship on Christmas Day as work.)

A GCSE Religious Studies 2010 examination paper was criticised for being insufficiently difficult. A picture of the Nativity was reproduced, showing two adults standing by the manger. Candidates were asked the taxing question: name the two people in the picture.

A maximum of two marks was awarded. This was in order to distinguish between those who could identify both mystery characters, and those who could name only one.

Christmas Number One Singles

1960	Cliff Richard and The Shadows	*I Love You*
1961	Danny Williams	*Moon River*
1962	Elvis Presley	*Return to Sender*

1963	The Beatles	*I Want to Hold Your Hand*
1964	The Beatles	*I Feel Fine*
1965	The Beatles	*Day Tripper / We Can Work It Out*
1966	Tom Jones	*Green, Green Grass of Home*
1967	The Beatles	*Hello, Goodbye*
1968	The Scaffold	*Lily the Pink*
1969	Rolf Harris	*Two Little Boys*
1970	Dave Edmunds	*I Hear You Knocking*
1971	Benny Hill	*Ernie (The Fastest Milkman in the West)*
1972	Jimmy Osmond	*Long Haired Lover from Liverpool*
1973	Slade	*Merry Xmas Everybody*
1974	Mud	*Lonely This Christmas*
1975	Queen	*Bohemian Rhapsody*
1976	Johnny Mathis	*When a Child is Born*
1977	Wings	*Mull of Kintyre*
1978	Boney M	*Mary's Boy Child / Oh My Lord*
1979	Pink Floyd	*Another Brick in the Wall (Part 2)*
1980	St Winifred's School Choir	*There's No-one Quite Like Grandma*
1981	The Human League	*Don't You Want Me*
1982	Renée and Renato	*Save Your Love*
1983	The Flying Pickets	*Only You*
1984	Band Aid	*Do They Know It's Christmas?*
1985	Shakin' Stevens	*Merry Christmas Everyone*
1986	Jackie Wilson	*Reet Petite*
1987	Pet Shop Boys	*Always on My Mind*
1988	Cliff Richard	*Mistletoe and Wine*

1989	Band Aid II	*Do They Know It's Christmas?*
1990	Cliff Richard	*Saviour's Day*
1991	Queen	*Bohemian Rhapsody / These Are the Days of Our Lives*
1992	Whitney Houston	*I Will Always Love You*
1993	Mr Blobby	*Mr Blobby*
1994	East 17	*Stay Another Day*
1995	Michael Jackson	*Earth Song*
1996	Spice Girls	*2 Become 1*
1997	Spice Girls	*Too Much*
1998	Spice Girls	*Goodbye*
1999	Westlife	*I Have a Dream / Seasons in the Sun*
2000	Bob the Builder	*Can We Fix It?*
2001	Robbie Williams and Nicole Kidman	*Somethin' Stupid*
2002	Girls Aloud	*Sound of the Underground*
2003	Michael Andrews and Gary Jules	*Mad World*
2004	Band Aid 20	*Do They Know It's Christmas?*
2005	Shayne Ward	*That's My Goal*
2006	Leona Lewis	*A Moment Like This*
2007	Leon Jackson	*When You Believe*
2008	Alexandra Burke	*Hallelujah*
2009	Rage Against the Machine	*Killing in the Name*
2010	Matt Cardle	*When We Collide*

Queen Victoria and Prince Albert regularly ate swan for Christmas dinner.

Early Christian legends

Some early Christian writings give extra 'details' to the Christmas story. The Protoevangelium of James, dating from about 145 AD, says Mary went into labour while she and Joseph were travelling to Bethlehem. Joseph found a cave and went off to find a midwife, who was present when Jesus was born; the cave itself was illuminated by a miraculous, brilliant light. The midwife told the story to a colleague called Salome, who didn't believe that a virgin could bear a child. As a punishment for Salome's faithlessness, her hand withered, but it was cured when she touched the baby. The Protoevangelium also states that Joseph was a widower, much older than Mary, who had children by his first wife: these were the brothers and sisters of Jesus mentioned in the Gospels (e.g. Mark 6.1-6).

Pseudo-Matthew is much later, dating from around 600. It gives the first known mention of the ox and the ass at the stable. The Syriac Infancy Gospel, which seems to be a little earlier, attests to a conversation the baby Jesus had with Mary. It claims he told his mother, 'I am Jesus, the Son of God, the Word, to whom you gave birth, as the

Angel Gabriel told you. My Father has sent me for the salvation of the world.' The infant Jesus also performed a number of miracles in Egypt.

Documents like these are much later than the New Testament Gospels. With the exceptions of the ox and the ass, and the idea of Joseph's being older than Mary (and possibly a widower with children), they have had little influence on mainstream Christianity.

Perhaps just as well.

A type of snail discovered on Mba Island, Fiji, in 1976 was given the scientific name *Ba humbugi*.

Episodes of *Doctor Who* broadcast on Christmas Day

1965: *The Feast of Steven*

William Hartnell played the Doctor; his companions were Steven (Peter Purves – yes, the one who was on *Blue Peter*) and Jean Marsh from *Upstairs Downstairs* as Sara Kingdom.

The Feast of Steven was part of the 12 part epic, *The Daleks' Master Plan*. In fact, the story took a break for

Christmas Day, with a comedy runaround which saw the *Tardis* land on the set of a silent movie, where the regulars were chased by the Keystone Kops and met Charlie Chaplin. The Daleks did not feature, which must have spoilt Christmas for the children in the audience (who'd today be in their fifties and have presumably now recovered from the trauma).

The episode is notorious for the ending: Hartnell turned to the camera and wished everyone at home a Happy Christmas.

Audience: 7.9 million.

The next Christmas Day special was 40 years later. When Jon Pertwee and Tom Baker played the Doctor in the 1970s, edited compilations of some stories were shown during the Christmas holidays (though never on Christmas Day). These included *Genesis of the Daleks*, which introduced the character of Davros.

2005: *The Christmas Invasion*

David Tennant played the Doctor; his companion was Rose (Billie Piper).

This was Tennant's first full episode; he appeared briefly at the end of the previous season, inheriting the *Tardis* from Christopher Eccleston. The Doctor spent most of the story asleep and possibly dying as he tried to recover from swapping his body, but he woke up in time to defeat an attempted invasion by the Sycorax.

It also featured a killer Christmas tree and homicidal robot Santas.

Audience: 9.8 million.

2006: *The Runaway Bride*

David Tennant again. The guest companion was Donna (Catherine Tate guest starring, though she returned to the series a year later as a regular).

The Doctor saved the day by outwitting a very, very big spider.
Audience: 9.3 million.

2007: *Voyage of the Damned*
David Tennant. Guest companion this time was Astrid, played by someone called Kylie Minogue. The baddie was Max, a megalomaniac in a wheelchair. (Not to be confused with Davros, a megalomaniac in a wheelchair.)
Audience: 13.3 million.

2008: *The Next Doctor*
David Tennant, flying solo for his last few stories. David Morrisey played Jackson Lake, a Victorian who laboured under the misapprehension that he was, in fact, the Doctor. Baddies: Cybermen.
Audience: 13.1 million.

2009: *The End of Time* (part one)
David Tennant's final story. The second episode was broadcast on New Year's Day 2010, with Tennant regenerating into Matt Smith. The companion was Wilfred Mott, played by Bernard Cribbins. 43 years earlier, Cribbins played another companion of the Doctor: Tom Campbell in the snappily titled film *Daleks – Invasion Earth 2150 AD*, alongside the great Peter Cushing as Dr Who. (*Doctor Who* fans are fairly sniffy about this film because it was a remake. The original starred William Hartnell and, despite its crummy special effects, was actually much better.)
Epic stuff. The Master was played by John Simm. The Time Lords featured and their boss was Timothy Dalton.
Audience: 11.5 million.

2010: *A Christmas Carol.*
Matt Smith as the eleventh Doctor. Companions were

Amy (Karen Gillan) and Rory (Arthur Darvill), though they were rather eclipsed by guest star Katherine Jenkins. The plot was a clever rewrite of the Dickens story, with Michael Gambon superb as the Scrooge character, Kazran Sardik.

Audience: 12.1 million.

Extract from Kilvert's Diary

The Reverend Francis Kilvert was curate to the Reverend Richard Lister Venables, Vicar of Clyro in Radnorshire (now Powys). The diary extract comes from 1870, when Kilvert was 31.

Sunday, Christmas Day

As I lay awake praying in the early morning I thought I heard a sound of distant bells. It was an intense frost. I sat down in my bath upon a sheet of thick ice which broke in the middle into large pieces whilst sharp points and jagged edges stuck all round the sides of the tub like chevaux de frise, not particularly comforting to the naked thighs and loins, for the keen ice cut like broken glass. The ice water stung and scorched like fire. I had to collect the floating pieces of ice and pile them on a chair before I could use the sponge and then I had to thaw the sponge in my hands for it was a mass of ice. The morning was most brilliant. Walked to the Sunday School with Gibbing – and the road sparkled with millions of rainbows, the seven colours gleaming in every glittering point of hoar frost.

The Church was very cold in spite of two roaring stove fires. Mr V. preached and went to Bettws.

Monday, 26 December

Much warmer and almost a thaw. Left Clyro at 11 a.m.

At Chippenham my father and John were on the platform. After dinner we opened a hamper of game sent by the Venables, and found in it a pheasant, a hare, a brace of rabbits, a brace of woodcocks, and a turkey. Just like them, and their constant kindness.

Tuesday, 27 December

After dinner drove into Chippenham with Perch and bought a pair of skates at Benk's for 17/6. Across the fields to the Draycot water and the young Awdry ladies chaffed me about my new skates. I had not been on skates since I was here last, 5 years ago, and was very awkward for the first ten minutes, but the knack soon came again. There was a distinguished company on the ice, Lady Dangan, Lord and Lady Royston and Lord George Paget all skating. Also Lord and Lady Sydney and a Mr Calcroft, whom they all of course called the Hangman. I had the honour of being knocked down by Lord Royston, who was coming round suddenly on the outside edge. A large fire of logs burning within an enclosure of wattled hurdles. Harriet Awdry skated beautifully and jumped over a half sunken punt. Arthur Law skating jumped over a chair on its legs.

Wednesday, 28 December

An inch of snow fell last night and as we walked to Draycot to skate the snow storm began again. As we passed Langley Burrell Church we heard the strains of the quadrille band on the ice at Draycot. The afternoon grew murky and when we began to skate the air was thick with falling snow. But it soon stopped and gangs of labourers were at work immediately sweeping away the new fallen snow and skate cuttings of ice. The Lancers was beautifully skated. When it grew dark the ice was lighted with Chinese lanterns, and the intense glare of blue, green, and crimson lights and magnesium riband made the whole place as light as day. Then people skated with torches.

Thursday, 29 December

Skating at Draycot again with Perch. Fewer people on the ice today. No quadrille band, torches or fireworks, but it was very pleasant, cosy and sociable. Yesterday when the Lancers was being skated Lord Royston was directing the figures. Harriet Awdry corrected him in one figure and he was quite wrong. But he immediately left the quadrille and sat down sulking on the bank, saying to one of his friends, 'Those abominable Miss Awdrys have contradicted me about the Lancers.' This was overheard and repeated to Harriet by a mutual friend, and the next time she saw him she said meaningly, 'Lord Royston, sometimes remarks are overheard and repeated,' or something to that effect. However, soon after he wanted to make it up and asked her to skate up the ice hand in hand with him. 'Certainly not, Lord Royston,' she said. Lady Royston skates very nicely and seems very nice. A sledge chair was put on the ice and Lady Royston and Lady Dangan, Margaret, Fanny, Maria, and Harriet Awdry were drawn about in it by turns, Charles Awdry pushing behind and Edmund and Arthur and Walter pulling with ropes. It was a capital team and went at a tremendous pace up and down the ice.

Things that really happened at Nativity plays

Finding enough roles for over a hundred children isn't easy, so some schools ask most children to come as one of the animals in the stable. One little boy turned up clad from head to toe in black velvet. He was the Christmas bat.

At another school, the animals included a dragon.

And a crab.

Controversy and dark mutterings were caused in one school when the rôle of Mary went to the daughter of the PTA chair...

Some teachers take the view that the part of Gabriel should be given to the girl who should have played Mary but whose parents are less trouble.

Mumsnet had a discussion on how to make a costume for the nativity play character of Mince Pie.

One innkeeper was supposed to look into the crib and say, 'Isn't it amazing that this tiny baby will be saviour of the world?' He forgot his line and substituted it with, 'Ooh, isn't he like his father?'

Another ad lib: a five year old introduced Mary as Jesus' au pair.

Misheard lyrics: 'deep pan, crisp and even'; 'the cattle are glowing, the baby awakes'; 'Away in a manger, two quid for a bed'; 'O little town of Beverley Hen'.

Tinsel

Tinsel was invented in Nuremberg in about 1610 and was originally made from silver and, later, from fool's gold or pyrite. It was used to decorate statues before it decorated Christmas trees. As it was expensive, it was beyond most people's means until aluminium was used in the early twentieth century. However, the aluminised paper was flammable; the tree lights and the tinsel could prove a dangerous combination.

Modern tinsel is usually made out of PVC.

Things that happened on Christmas Day

274: The Roman Emperor Aurelian made the cult of Sol Invictus ('the Unconquered Sun') an official cult.

800: Charlemagne crowned as Holy Roman Emperor.

1066: William the Conqueror was crowned King of England.

1223: St Francis invented the Christmas crib in Greccio, using a stable and live animals.

1642: Birth of Isaac Newton.

1644: Christmas was banned by Act of Parliament. The

Puritans thought it was an excuse for a booze up and was therefore a bad thing. Plum puddings, mince pies and holly were made illegal.

1818: Premiere in Boston of Handel's *Messiah*.

1868: President Andrew Johnson pardoned all Confederate soldiers.

1899: Birth of Humphrey Bogart.

1914: Christmas truce in the First World War.

1938: Death of science fiction author Karel Čapek, who coined the word 'robot'.

1945: Birth of Kenny Everett.

1946: Death of W. C. Fields.

1954: Birth of Annie Lennox.

1957: Birth of Shane MacGowan.

1974: Cyclone Tracy devastated the city of Darwin in Australia

1977: Menachem Begin of Israel met Anwar Sadat of Egypt, beginning the peace accord between the countries.

Death of Charlie Chaplin (also in 1977).

1978: Birth of Simon Jones, cricketer.

1984: Birth of Alistair Cook, cricketer.

1989: Vaclav Havel elected President of Czechoslovakia.

1990: First successful test run of something that was later called the Internet.

1991: Mikhail Gorbachev resigned as President of the USSR.

1995: Death of Dean Martin.

2003: Beagle 2, the British-built Mars probe, should have landed on Mars but disappeared instead.

What the British think

A survey of UK adults was conducted by the polling and research organisation ComRes in 2007. The poll was commissioned by the theology think-tank Theos. It found:

83% knew where Jesus was said to be born. 56% believed that Jesus genuinely was born in Bethlehem.

73% knew that an angel told Mary she would give birth to Jesus.

48% knew that John the Baptist was Jesus' cousin.

22% knew that Mary, Joseph and Jesus fled to Egypt to escape Herod.

34% believed in the virgin conception of Jesus (the figures vary according to gender: 39% of women and 29% of men). 32% of adults thought the virgin birth was not historically true.

28% believed the angels genuinely visited the shepherds; 32% thought it was fictional.

37% believed that the massacre of the innocents (the killing of the children by King Herod) was historically accurate.

52% said that the birth of Jesus was of personal significance to them; 72% said it was culturally significant.

57% said they would consider that, when they celebrated Christmas, they were celebrating it as a religious festival.

When the figures are broken down further, 66% of Scots consider that they celebrate Christmas as a religious festival.

48% of men and 36% of women do not consider that they are celebrating the religious aspect of Christmas.

ComRes conducted another survey for Theos in 2009. A representative sample of adults was asked to respond to a number of statements:

'Christmas should be renamed to reflect our multicultural society.' 84% disagreed.

'Christmas should be called Christmas, even though we are no longer a Christian country.' 77% agreed.

'Christmas should be called Christmas, because we are still a Christian country.' 85% agreed.

Christmas turkeys

Turkeys have a good pedigree: they have been on the planet for a long time.

Some 23 million years after their first appearance, in the sixteenth century to be precise, they became standard fare on the British Christmas menu. Before then, peacock or boar were more common. (Before the sixteenth century, not before 23 million years ago.)

Ten Pantomime facts

1. The first pantomime is said to have been *Cinderalla* in 1804, at Drury Lane.
2. Christmas pantomimes have never really caught on in the United States and are rarely performed there.
3. The tradition of the Good Fairy entering from stage right and the baddie entering from stage left may go back to medieval mystery plays. Stage right symbolised heaven and stage left symbolised hell.
4. There is a long tradition of girls playing boys in British theatre and music hall, and principal boys developed from this. It also gave men in Victorian audiences an excuse to see women in shorts and tights, rather than in the modest attire characteristic of the times.
5. And, of course, men or boys played all the female rôles in Shakespeare's time, so drag has a good pedigree. Joseph Grimaldi was one of the earliest dames in an 1820 production of *Cinderella*.
6. Christopher Biggins played a pantomime dame every year for 38 years, until 2007.
7. Some Victorian pantomimes were five hours long.
8. And had up to 600 people in the cast.
9. They also employed actors who specialised in playing animals; non-human roles were known as 'skin parts'.
10. Charlie Chaplin played the front end of the horse at the Hippodrome Theatre in Stockport.

The most watched Christmas programme in the history of British television was *Mike Yarwood's Christmas Show* in 1977, with 28 million viewers: half the population of the UK at the time. It was only just ahead of *The Morecambe and Wise Christmas Special* of the same year.

Extract from *Father and Son*

Edmund Gosse

The Victorian writer and critic Edmund Gosse was brought up by his widowed father, a respected biologist, in a strict non conformist household. In this extract, Gosse looks back to Christmas 1857, when he was eight.

On the subject of all feasts of the Church he [Gosse's father] held views of an almost grotesque peculiarity. He looked upon each of them as nugatory and worthless, but the keeping of Christmas appeared to him by far the most hateful, and nothing less than an act of idolatry. 'The very word is Popish,' he used to exclaim, 'Christ's Mass!' pursing up his lips with the gesture of one who tastes assafoetida by accident. Then he would adduce the antiquity of the so-called feast, adapted from horrible heathen rites, and itself a soiled relic of the abominable

Yule-Tide. He would denounce the horrors of Christmas until it almost made me blush to look at a holly-berry.

On Christmas Day of this year 1857 our villa saw a very unusual sight. My Father had given strictest charge that no difference whatever was to be made in our meals on that day; the dinner was to be neither more copious than usual nor less so. He was obeyed, but the servants, secretly rebellious, made a small plum-pudding for themselves... Early in the afternoon, the maids, – of whom we were now advanced to keeping two, – kindly remarked that 'the poor dear child ought to have a bit, anyhow', and wheedled me into the kitchen, where I ate a slice of plum-pudding. Shortly I began to feel that pain inside which in my frail state was inevitable, and my conscience smote me violently. At length I could bear my spiritual anguish no longer, and bursting into the study I called out: 'Oh! Papa, Papa, I have eaten of flesh offered to idols!' It took some time, between my sobs, to explain what had happened. Then my Father sternly said: 'Where is the accursed thing?' I explained that as much as was left of it was still on the kitchen table. He took me by the hand, and ran with me into the midst of the startled servants, seized what remained of the pudding, and with the plate in one hand and me still tight in the other, ran till we reached the dust-heap, when he flung the idolatrous confectionery on to the middle of the ashes, and then raked it deep down into the mass. The suddenness, the violence, the velocity of this extraordinary act made an impression on my memory which nothing will ever efface.

Note: assafoetida was a nasty tasting resin that was used as a medicine.

According to Which?, more than 11 million people in the UK have trouble fitting the Christmas turkey into the oven.

Actors who have played Ebenezer Scrooge

They include:

Tom Ricketts (1908)
Reginald Owen (1938)
Alistair Sim (1951)
Basil Rathbone (1956)
Wilfrid Brambell (1966)
Albert Finney (1970)
Marcel Marceau (1973)
Michael Hordern (1977)
George C. Scott (1984)
Michael Caine (1992)
Tim Curry (1997)
Patrick Stewart (1999)
Kelsey Grammar (2004)
Jim Carrey (2009)

Alistair Sim's performance in the 1951 film *Scrooge* is often considered definitive.

In 2010, the Children's Society commissioned a survey. According to its results:

10% of adults think the religious meaning of Christmas is the most important thing.

When the figures are broken down further:

4% of 24-34 year olds thought the religious meaning was the most important;

20% of those aged over 60 thought it was the most important.

Yule

Yule was a Norse or Germanic ceremony, celebrating rebirth. Yule logs were burnt as part of the festivities. Mistletoe, holly and evergreens were believed to be the temporary homes of the woodland spirits who took shelter there when their normal homes had lost their leaves. Evergreens' significance was Christianised and they came to symbolise eternal life.

The Venerable Bede wrote that the pagan Anglo-Saxon year began on 25th December.

Extract from *The Diary of a Country Parson*

James Woodforde was Rector of Weston Longeville, Norfolk. This extract comes from 1794, when Woodforde was 54.

Woodforde tended to make notes of the money he spent; the way he wrote this down may need explanation today. So, 0.1.6 means 0 pounds, 1 shilling and sixpence. Woodforde's spelling and liberal use of capital letters have not been changed.

DEC. 25, Thursday, Xmas Day.

We breakfasted, dined, &c. again at home. It was very cold indeed this Morning, and the Snow in many Places quite deep, with an E. Wind. About 11 this Morning I walked to Church and read Prayers & administered the Holy Sacrament. Had but few Communicants the Weather so bad. Gave at the Altar for an Offering 0.2.6. Immediately after the Morning Service so far as before the administration of the H. Sacrament I was attacked with an Epileptic Fit, and fainted away in my Desk, but thank God! soon recovered and went through the remaining part of my duty. Mr. & Mrs. Girling, Mr. & Mrs. Howlett, Mr. St. Andrews, Mr. Hardy &c. &c. were much alarmed and were very kind to Me, during the fit and after. The Weather being so severely cold, which I could never escape from feeling its effect at all times, affected me so much this Morning, that made me faint away, what I always was afraid off for some Winters past, having often had many fears. Mr. Howlett after Service, very kindly offered to drive me home in his Cart, but as I was better I declined it, however hope that I shall not forget his civility. After Service was over, I walked into Mr. Stephen Andrew's House, and having warmed myself, I walked home and thank God, got home very well. Mr. Stephen Andrews & Family behaved very kindly. After I got home and had something warm to drink, I soon got tolerably well, but could only eat some plumb Pudding & a few Potatoes. Nancy was much alarmed when she first heard of it. Eliz. Case, Widow, Ned Howes, Thos. Atterton Senr., Christ. Dunnell, Robert Downing, and my Clerk Thos. Thurston, all dined at my House to day being Christmas Day, & each had a Shilling... A very fine Sirloin of Beef rosted and plenty of plumb Puddings for dinner & strong beer after. Took some Rhubarb going to bed.

DEC. 26, Friday

...Thank God! had a pretty good Night last Night, and I hope am something better, but rather languid & low. Could eat but very little for dinner to day. Appetite bad. To Weston Ringers, gave 0. 2. 6. To Christmas Boxes &c. gave 0. 4. 0. Dinner to day, Calfs Fry & a Rabbit rosted. I drank plentifully of Port Wine after dinner, instead of one Glass, drank 7 or 8 Wine Glasses, and it seemed to do me much good, being better for it.

Royal Institution Christmas Lectures

Since 1825, the Royal Institution has held annual lectures to convey scientific concepts in an entertaining way. They have been televised since 1966. Notable speakers have included Michael Faraday (19 times, beginning in 1827); Desmond Morris (1964); David Attenborough (1973); Heinz Wolff (1975); Carl Sagan (1977) and Richard Dawkins (1991).

Extract from *The Life of Our Lord* by Charles Dickens

Dickens wrote *The Life of Our Lord* in 1849. It was written for his children; Dickens did not intend it for a wider readership. In 1934, the Dickens family released it for publication.

This is Dickens' version of the nativity story.

My dear children, I am very anxious that you should know something about the History of Jesus Christ. For everybody ought to know about Him. No one ever lived, who was so good, so kind, so gentle, and so sorry for all people who did wrong, or were in anyway ill or miserable, as he was. And as he is now in Heaven, where we hope to go, and all to meet each other after we are dead, and there be happy always together, you never can think what a good place Heaven, is without knowing who he was and what he did.

He was born, a long long time ago – nearly Two Thousand years ago – at a place called Bethlehem. His father and mother lived in a city called Nazareth, but they were forced, by business to travel to Bethlehem. His father's name was Joseph, and his mother's name was

Mary.

And the town being very full of people, also brought there by business, there was no room for Joseph and Mary in the Inn or any house; so they went into a Stable to lodge, and in this stable Jesus Christ was born. There was no cradle or anything of that kind there, so Mary laid her pretty little boy in what is called the Manger, which is the place the horses eat out of. And there he fell asleep.

While he was asleep, some Shepherds who were watching Sheep in the Fields, saw an Angel from God, all light and beautiful, come moving over the grass towards Them. At first they were afraid and fell down and hid their faces. But it said, 'There is a child born to-day in the city of Bethlehem near here, who will grow up to be so good that God will love him as his own son; and he will teach men to love one another, and not to quarrel and hurt one another; and his name will be Jesus Christ; and people will put that name in their prayers, because they will know God loves it, and will know that they should love it too.' And then the Angel told the Shepherds to go to that Stable, and look at that little child in the Manger. Which they did; and they kneeled down by it in its sleep, and said, 'God bless this child!'

Now the great place of all that country was Jerusalem – just as London is the great place in England – and at Jerusalem the King lived, whose name was King Herod. Some wise men came one day, from a country a long way off in the East, and said to the King, 'We have seen a Star in the Sky, which teaches us to know that a child is born in Bethlehem who will live to be a man whom all people will love.' When King Herod heard this, he was jealous, for he was a wicked man. But he pretended not to be, and said to the wise men, 'Whereabouts is this child?' And the wise men said, 'We don't know. But we think the Star will shew us; for the Star has been moving on before us, all the way here, and is now standing still in the sky.' Then Herod asked them to see if the Star would shew them where the child lived, and ordered them, if they found the child, to come back to him. So they went out, and the Star went on, over their heads a little way before them, until it stopped over the house where the child was. This was very wonderful, but God ordered it to be so.

When the Star stopped, the wise men went in, and saw the child with Mary his Mother. They loved him very much, and gave him some presents. Then they went away. But they did not go back to King Herod; for they thought he was jealous, though he had not said so. So they went away, by night, back into their own country. And an Angel came, and told Joseph and Mary to take the child into a Country called Egypt, or Herod would kill him. So they escaped too, in the night – the father, the mother, and the child – and arrived there, safely.

But when this cruel Herod found that the wise men did not come back to him, and that he could not, therefore, find out where this child, Jesus Christ, lived, he called his soldiers and captains to him, and told them to go and Kill all the children in his dominions that were not more than two years old. The wicked men did so. The mothers of the children ran up and down the streets with them in their arms trying to save them, and hide them in caves and cellars, but it was of no use. The soldiers with their swords killed all the children they could find. This dreadful murder was called the Murder of the Innocents. Because the little children were so innocent.

King Herod hoped that Jesus Christ was one of them. But He was not, as you know, for He had escaped safely into Egypt. And he lived there, with his father and mother, until Bad King Herod died.

Traidcraft:
Stories of Christmas Around the World

Fiona Thomson

Christmas is an important time for Traidcraft, the UK's leading fair trade organisation, which has been fighting poverty through trade for more than 30 years. As a Christian-based organisation, it's a time when many staff celebrate the season – but the run-up to Christmas is also when thousands of parcels containing festive fair trade gifts, cards and foods are being dispatched from Traidcraft's Gateshead premises to customers across the UK.

These orders are vital for the producer groups in Africa, Asia and Latin America who make products or grow ingredients. Without these sales, many of them would not be able to provide for their families or educate their children.

Traidcraft doesn't just buy products: it creates partnerships and develops long-term relationships, planning and delivering projects which help people to develop skills and to get their voices heard. It's while meeting and working with producer groups and individuals that they have shared these stories of how they celebrate Christmas.

Bonus Day at St Mary's in Ahmedabad, India

Traidcraft works with people of all faiths and none, and St Mary's is a pioneering example of Muslims, Hindus and Christians working together in harmony.

St Mary's roots go back to the 1950s when a group of Dominican nuns from Spain arrived in the city to start a hospital. They found great poverty and homes without sanitation, poor hygiene and low life skills. Ahmedabad, which was famous for its textiles, suffered when most of the mills began to close in the 1980s and women became the sole earners.

Sister Lucia, who had enjoyed embroidery as a child in Spain, began running classes for women and children – trainees had to buy their own thread to ensure their commitment! Production began, leading to the sewing and embroidery centre, where women use traditional skills to make handicrafts.

Today, there are 400 women embroidering in their homes and 50 working at St Mary's – producing beautifully embroidered bags, cloths and accessories sold by Traidcraft and other organisations. One of the highlights of their year is Bonus Day, which takes place in the week leading up to Christmas.

Every person working for St Mary's receives their bonus gift, but there is also a full cultural programme of dancing and skits prepared by the women. Speeches are made and the annual review is presented. Guests are welcomed and there is also a moment of silence in memory of those who have died in the last year.

The bonus gift was originally something small, such as scissors, but the value has grown over the years. Now it can include a pressure cooker, jug, set of storage tins, blankets or towels.

There are 15 leaders in the different areas where the women work and they make recommendations on suitable gifts. These are then considered, along with the budget, and the gifts are bought. Women often bring members of their family with them to the celebrations, to help carry the gifts home.

Sushila Ashok has received Bonus Day gifts for more than 15 years. She joined St Mary's after attending their tailoring course. While she enjoys using some of the items, many are still untouched and in the boxes they were presented in.

'I am keeping them for my daughter when she gets married,' she said, explaining that many women do the same. 'If they take it they will remember what their mother gave them.'

Bonus Day is also a way of ensuring that the women receive quality items which they would not otherwise buy – and that is why they receive a practical gift instead of money.

'We would not be able to go and buy it with our own money,' Sushila said. 'If we have money in the hand we always try to buy something else for our family.'

For Christian women working at St Mary's there are other preparations to make. During Advent, they remove all the brass jugs and vessels from the shelves in their homes, then whitewash the walls and rearrange the displays.

Kokila Parmar, who has worked at St Mary's for more than 20 years, is a member of St Joseph's Roman Catholic church in the neighbouring parish. She described how she gets ready for Christmas.

'We make sweets. We go a little early during the weekdays of Christmas week to prepare the decoration of the house. We whitewash the house. We have a crib in the house and put up the star and then a series of lights.'

Kokila is a widow and spends Christmas with her teenage son, Joyal, who was just 18 months old when his father Pius died from tuberculosis. Her wages from St Mary's were the main income for the family while Pius was ill. Since then, she has been able to save some money and this – together with a loan she will take out from St Mary's – will help Joyal to continue his studies when he leaves school.

Ask Kokila what work for St Mary's means for her and she says: 'Life. For both of us, life. The main hope is my son, because I have no other in the family; that he may study well and get a good job.'

Her appreciation of St Mary's is made even stronger by the fact that when orders were low she decided to work elsewhere and took a job in a canteen.

'The salaries were not paid on time,' she said. 'Even when we went to the toilet we had the fear.' (As well as worrying that they will lose wages for taking time away from work, women's toilet facilities are not always close by or in areas where they feel safe.)

Her new job lasted only a month and then she returned to St Mary's. So what does she appreciate about working here?

'The freedom. This is like a house, we feel at home. We feel safe.'

And will she leave St Mary's and look for another job? Kokila laughs and says a definite 'No!' She wants to be joining in the Bonus Day celebrations for many years to come.

Hampers to share at Crisil, Bolivia

It's not just at St Mary's where workers receive practical gifts at Christmas. Crisil, the Bolivian glass factory which supplies Traidcraft with handmade glass products, also helps its staff to celebrate.

Each worker receives a hamper that includes a chicken, a bottle of wine and toys for any children aged 12 or under. The gift is presented in a large bowl, so even the container can be put to good use once the contents are used.

For couples like Gregorio Yupanqi and his wife, Concepcion, this means they have two hampers to take home!

Gregorio specialises in making wine glasses and Concepcion packs the finished products. The regular income the couple receive from Crisil has helped them to build their own home, which they share with their four children and other family members, so there are plenty of people to enjoy the contents of their hampers.

'Food is our most expensive item,' Gregorio said, describing how they celebrate Christmas. 'We cook milk and chocolate [to make a hot chocolate drink] and have bunuelos [a traditional type of fritter] on Christmas Eve.'

Gifts and tea at Ndima, Kenya

Purity Muthoni and her husband, William Mathenge, are tea farmers in Kenya. They sell their tea to Ndima Factory, which supplies Traidcraft. For them, church is an important part of life throughout the year. Purity preaches and is a leading figure in the Mothers' Union, both in Mathia Anglican Church and the wider area.

So what happens in her home at Christmas?

'We celebrate with our family. Our daughters, our daughters' husbands and their children, they come here on the 25th and we eat together. We celebrate the day and we have tea.'

She explained the types of food that they eat. 'Chicken, goat, rice, chapati, sweet potato. We exchange gifts with everybody. My daughter brings me a leso [rectangular cloth worn by women]. My husband might get a suit.'

Tea not only provides the Ndima farmers with an income: it is at the heart of all their church celebrations, as tea farmer Patricia Mutangili explained.

'Sometimes we combine with local neighbouring churches. We must have tea. There is no church gathering without tea.

'We have a kitchen and sometimes make things and eat together. When we celebrate we put poems together and songs and each group has to produce something. The men's group produced a poem.'

Patricia, who attends Mathia Roman Catholic church,

described their Christmas celebrations. 'Usually we have a service here on Christmas Eve. We decorate the church with ribbons and balloons and create the nativity story. We sing Christmas carols and it is very great. On Christmas Eve the church is usually full.'

From Shining Path to Shining Star, Peru

Peruvian craftworkers Sirci Marquez and her husband, Alberto, may celebrate Christmas far from where they grew up, but their generosity ensures that children in Alberto's home town are also able to celebrate.

The couple, who live near Lima in Peru, work with Allpa – one of Traidcraft's suppliers - and make ceramic models and nativity sets, complete with the star above the stable. It's these sales that help them to give Christmas gifts not just to their own son and daughter, but to children in Quinua, Ayacucho, where Albert grew up.

'Some of the ways that we celebrate Christmas is we send some money for the people who live in Quinua for them to celebrate with some gifts,' Alberto said. 'We share a part of what we have. It is most important for us to say that our purpose is not only to sell and produce things but to make sure that part of our earnings goes to this.

Sirci added: 'I think because we believe in sharing with people still living in Quinua, it is important to send things for them.'

Although they remember their home towns fondly, life there was not always easy. It was the threat of the Shining Path, the Maoist terrorist organisation, which led to their families fleeing their homes and brought them to Lima in the 1980s.

Sirci is a native of Santa Ana, a small village 90 minutes by road from the city of La Merced in the jungle fringe area of the Department of Junin. Like many local people, her family earned a living from fruit farming. But in 1985, when Sirci was eight, the political violence and recruitment of young people to Shining Path led the family to move to Lima, with only the few belongings they were able to carry with them.

'We left because of the Shining Path terrorism,' Sirci said. 'They almost got two of my brothers. We had to be safe.'

The family built a small house, using straw mats as flooring, and Sirci's father, who remained on his Santa Ana farm, sent fruit that Sirci's mother sold at the local and wholesale markets. Sirci and her brothers also helped to sell the produce to pay for their studies. When Sirci finished school she began studying at Union University, but did not complete her education and went on to work in textile manufacturing.

Her husband, Alberto Marcapina, is a native of Quinua, Ayacucho. He also came to Lima with his family to flee the violence in their area.

'At that time we had to escape,' he said, 'because if you were a man it was worse. They wanted to recruit you by force and there was not a place where you could work safely.'

Alberto came from a family of potters and during his first years in Lima he worked in his brother Romulo's workshop. Then, in 1990, he began working on his own and made his home and workshop in Santa Clara, which is where he and Sirci live. The couple met in 1995 and married a year later. When their first child, Alberto, was born, Sirci stopped working in textiles and got involved in the workshop.

Alberto taught Sirci the art of ceramics and little by little her skills developed until she took charge of the workshop. They expanded their line of products and developed a new technique for making the popular nativity scenes, which raised production from 50 to 200 a day.

The couple work in partnership: Alberto creates new

models and carves the moulds while Sirci deals with clients, administration, buying materials and supervising workers.

'I am very happy at Christmas,' said Alberto, 'both of us, because we feel that when other people get our work they see the Peruvian traditional way reflected in our work.'

For Alberto, childhood Christmases rarely included gifts or meals, but church was very much part of the tradition.

'In Quinua, because we didn't have the income, we celebrated the baby Jesus. For most people who live in that area, a special meal was not even possible and when we came to Lima, we did improve our Christmas,' Alberto said. 'One of the things I remember at that time was that we went to church at midnight Mass. I remember that very well, because even though we did not have anything to celebrate in the home, we did not forget to go to church.'

Giving thanks at EAC, South Africa

For raisin farmers at Eksteenskuil Agricultural Co-operative in the Northern Cape, South Africa, 21st December 2002 is a date that they will always remember. On that day, a hailstorm wiped out 70% of their vines – when they were just weeks away from the harvest.

Grapes are one of the few crops that earn money for the farmers who live on islands in the Orange River, near the Kalahari Desert, but the hailstorms caused heavy crop losses for that year and the next.

Traidcraft, which had been working with the farmers since 1996, began working with them to assess the size of the problem. The farmers organised emergency aid for families whose homes were damaged and Traidcraft made an advance payment, some of which provided short-term loans to help local farmers.

Traidcraft also agreed to buy all the remaining grapes,

guaranteeing at least some income from their diminished harvest.

Since then, the group has continued supplying dried fruit to Traidcraft and, with support from Traidcraft, became suppliers of the world's first Fairtrade raisins. They have also suffered extreme weather conditions, such as recent flooding, but they have never forgotten how they recovered from the hailstorm and hold a thanksgiving service every year.

Farmer Nelie Kok explained that they alternate the services between the different churches and denominations every year.

'This service has come about as a result of the hailstorm that happened on 21st December 2002,' he said. 'The first one was held in 2003, after we had not received any assistance from government. Since then it is being held on the Sunday closest to that date.'

Local church choirs take part in the thanksgiving service and it provides the perfect start to the farmers' own Christmas celebrations in their homes.

Faith, family and food

These snapshots from around the world show how faith, family and food are at the heart of Christmas celebrations – wherever people live.

Even those who do not celebrate Christmas benefit from our UK celebrations, as many craftworkers have helped to create the beautiful Traidcraft decorations which adorn our Christmas trees and homes.

They include people like Gyassudin, a Muslim, who makes embroidered zari decorations for Tara Projects in India. 'The craft group has enabled me to survive and earn enough money to support my children,' he said.

Raissudin, who also works in the zari group, explained:

'This is our traditional craft. When we hear that this is going to another country, to be used as a holy decoration, that makes us happy.'